THE NATURAL HISTORY OF RIVERS

THE NATURAL HISTORY
OF RIVERS

by

RON FREETHY

TERENCE DALTON LIMITED
LAVENHAM . SUFFOLK
1986

Published by
TERENCE DALTON LIMITED
ISBN 0 86138 045 2

Text photoset in 11/12pt Baskerville

Printed in Great Britain at
The Lavenham Press Limited, Lavenham, Suffolk

Contents

Chapter One   Introduction   1

Chapter Two   The Headstream to the Middle Reaches   ...   21

Chapter Three   The Middle Reaches   39

Chapter Four   The Lower Reaches and Estuary   55

Chapter Five   Plants of the River   67

Chapter Six   Invertebrates   89

Chapter Seven   The Arthropods   111

Chapter Eight   Fish of the River   139

Chapter Nine   Birds of River and Marsh   159

Chapter Ten   Riverside Mammals   179

Chapter Eleven   River Conservation   193

Bibliography   204

Index   207

CHAPTER ONE

Introduction

THE living material which makes up all organisms contains at least sixty per cent water and therefore requires a regular supply of unpolluted water.

Water supply was vital to human settlements, which sprang up along river banks and on estuaries fed by freshwater streams. Trading journeys were made much more safely and easily by following a watercourse rather than by attempting a perilous journey through swampy or heavily wooded country. It did not take long for man to develop simple boats to take advantage of tidal rivers and be carried upstream to inland settlements.

The idea of making the upper reaches navigable evolved gradually; shallow fords were just as much a nuisance to traffic heading upriver in dry weather as they were to those trying to cross in times of flood. Bridges were built to span watercourses and shallow spots were deepened to allow easier passage; thus was the concept of river management born. This was bound to affect both the population and distribution of aquatic organisms.

The idea of extracting drinking water from points upstream and the disposal of waste downstream was only feasible when small populations were involved; many medieval towns had clean water running into the rich areas, but that same water was filthy by the time it reached the poorer areas situated downstream. This pollution, however, was relatively localised and the river quickly recovered as its waters flowed through long stretches of unpopulated countryside. The growth of large settlements with huge industrial complexes belching out pollutants did not become a major problem until the nineteenth century and was not tackled seriously until the latter part of the twentieth century.

A glance at any relief map will show clearly that no two rivers are alike, even if they are geographically quite close together over much of their length, and even if they share the same estuary. This has not prevented geographers and natural historians from attempting to classify various zones, and it has to be admitted that the idea of river zones does make it easier to describe the fauna and flora occurring along a river's length. The idea originated in continental Europe; some workers have

Sentinel of the river, a grey heron stands in the shallows watching for fish. *Michael Edwards* worked out highly complicated schemes with many zones and sub-zones, but as long ago as 1928 Kathleen Carpenter simplified these and produced a four-zone system for British rivers.

River zoning

Carpenter suggested that many rivers begin with a headstream which is typified by low temperature and sometimes, but not essentially, a torrential flow. This area is not very rich in life, though the occasional stonefly larva and brown trout can survive in this tempestuous habitat. The headstream then widens out into a fast-flowing torrent, often fed from several tributaries. The only fish which is able to survive for most of its life by swimming against the current in this zone is the brown trout (*Salmo trutta*), and hence Carpenter called this the Troutbeck. Some organisms seek shelter between and beneath stones in this part of the river and the bullhead or miller's thumb (*Cottus gobio*) is often found in this position.

A headstream in the Lancashire Pennines carves out a channel through the rocky terrain.

Ron Freethy

Slowly but surely the precocious young river begins to slow down; silt and mud begins to accumulate on its bed and vegetation such as the water crowfoot (*Ranunculus fluitans*) can establish itself. It is this region that continental workers refer to as the Grayling Zone; Carpenter was of the opinion that the grayling (*Thymallus thymallus*) was not sufficiently widespread in Britain to be honoured by its own zone and she labelled this area the Minnow Reach, since this is a region in which minnows (*Phoxinus phoxinus*) are often found.

Minnows be blowed! I know many British anglers who would say that fishing for grayling is one of the greatest thrills of their sport; this fish, which does occur regularly, is such a sporting fighter as well as being pleasing to the palate. Strong fighting fish such as salmon, trout and grayling thrive in these richly oxygenated waters, but coarse fish are not usually present until the river becomes slow and meandering.

As the current slows down solid material falls to the bottom and the muddy bed and shallow recesses so produced allow rooted vegetation to thrive. The continental workers refer to this area as the Bream Zone, but Carpenter preferred the term Lowland Reach. Many species of fish are found here including roach (*Rutilus rutilus*), bream (*Abramis brama*), rudd (*Scardinius erythrophthalmus*), chub (*Leuciscus cephalus*) and three-spined stickleback (*Gasterosteus aculeatus*).

Obviously this basic pattern will vary according to the nature of the local topography. Some rivers which rise in low hills will not develop racing torrents and the zones so beloved of the trout and the grayling will be absent. On the other hand the presence of a waterfall can create these conditions below an area which could almost be classified as a Lowland Reach, forming what amounts to a second Troutbeck. Outflows from man-made reservoirs pouring through sluices create zones which, however artificial they may be, are very real to the fish and the animals they feed upon, as do weirs along watercourses.

In addition to local topography the geology of a particular region will have another, and in many ways more profound, influence on the water. Rivers of the chalk and limestone districts abound in the essential minerals needed by crustaceans and molluscs to build up their skeletons. These in turn form a nutritious diet for fish, especially trout, and chalky rivers such as the Itchen in Hampshire are impressive fisheries precisely for this reason.

Rivers are far too valuable in human affairs to be left alone. Stretches too shallow to be navigable may be deepened, bends difficult to manoeuvre straightened, narrows widened and vegetation removed. As we have seen, river management is not a new concept and was frequently resorted to by civilisations even earlier than that of Rome. As towns grew,

Weirs such as this one on the River Leven at Newby Bridge, Cumbria, can increase oxygen levels and encourage trout and grayling.
Ron Freethy

raw sewage poured into rivers; initially this was no bad thing for wildlife since fertiliser is just as useful to aquatic vegetation as it is to terrestrial crops. The rich vegetation so produced added to the problems of silting up and watercourses became difficult to penetrate without the implementation of extensive and expensive methods of weed control.

As towns became cities the light shower of sewage became a deluge; because the breakdown of effluent requires an appreciable amount of oxygen, the water became deficient in this vital gas. Initially the large, active fish were affected, and then all animal life perished in what eventually degenerated into open stinking sewers. From 1750 onwards the Industrial Revolution began to gain momentum and factories involved in the dyeing and bleaching of fabrics, chemical works, heavy industrial complexes and mining concerns all added their lethal load to many of our dying rivers.

Extensive pollution was born a lusty infant indeed. Hopefully it is now past middle age and may soon begin to lose some strength, although it will probably be a long time a-dying.

Sophisticated and expensive treatment plants have done much to reduce the effect of sewage pollution, and at the present time two of the most disturbing aspects of river pollution are run-offs from mining projects and the insensitive use of herbicides, fungicides and insecticides. Commercial mining on a large scale is essential to our existence, but it most certainly poses a great threat to life in our watercourses. Particles of coal dust can smother the gill surfaces of fish and coat the leaves of plants to such an extent that they are unable to carry out their normal photosynthetic activities and they too perish, thus disrupting the chain of life at the first linkage.

The discharge of heavy metals such as lead, copper and mercury is well known, but even this is more easily dealt with than what is known as acid mine drainage, which is so much a feature of areas where there is a high sulphur content in the rock. In these conditions dilute but still effective sulphuric acid is formed beneath the ground from oxygen, water and sulphur, a meeting which it is all but impossible to prevent. The resulting streams may surface miles from the source of pollution years after the workings have closed; those responsible for paying for the clearing-up operations may have been long dead. Although water laden with sulphuric acid may sometimes be clear, the tell-tale sign is usually a deep yellowish-brown colour due to dissolved iron.

During a waterway survey carried out by the British Trust for Ornithology an area called Lochty Burn in Fife was discovered to be badly polluted as a direct result of acid–ferruginous run-off from an open-cast mine. Along 2.8 kilometres of its length the burn had once supported seventeen bird breeding territories, thirteen of these belonging to reed buntings (*Emberiza schoeniclus*). By 1975 the count had fallen to eight and in 1976 it was down to four. Apart from the effect on the bird life the loss of amenity value must also be commented upon. Even in highly polluted areas some plants, especially algae, can survive and the bulrush (*Typha latifolia*) seems surprisingly resistant.

Many pollutants may not in fact be poisonous; even hot water can be a problem in some rivers. The fact that oxygen is much less soluble in hot water than in cold can result in hot water discharged into a watercourse forming an impenetrable barrier for migratory fish attempting to pass through on their way to spawning grounds — these active fish require water rich in oxygen. Other factories, those involved in the production of china clay, for example, may cause turbidity in the water, cutting down clarity and preventing the growth of plants and thus reducing the dependent animal life. Insecticides such as DDT and other organochlorines sprayed on to farmlands and roadside verges eventually find their way into watercourses where the effect is immediate on some species, while on others such as the larger fish, birds and mammals and ultimately, perhaps, ourselves it may be much more gradual. Biologists are often able to gauge the level of pollution by reference to the species of animal found in an area.

The use of waterways as transportation routes was vital until the coming of the railway age in the middle of the nineteenth century, and manufacturers of the eighteenth century preferred waterborne transport to a bumpy and potentially destructive journey by waggon along the turnpike system. Obviously the transport of delicate products such as pottery was almost impossible by road. Navigable rivers were few and a Shropshire company in 1775 transported pig iron by a roundabout route of some 400 miles of river, sea and river again rather than risk a journey of 60 miles overland. By the end of the eighteenth century Britain's rapidly expanding industries were crying out for more navigable waterways such as the canals already constructed by potential competitors in Holland and France. There is a case for briefly mentioning canals since they were constructed to join rivers and they thus allowed movement not only of boats but of wildlife from one river to another.

The Canal Age

Canal building in Britain was initially the story of one man with money and foresight and of another with an iron will and a highly inventive mind. Francis Egerton, who became the Duke of Bridgewater (1736–1803), was well educated, extremely rich and with an ambition to become richer. James Brindley, whose shorter life stretched from 1716 to 1772, was a man of much humbler origins who apparently never learned to read or write with any degree of fluency; he spent the early part of his working life as a wheelwright. He became the Duke of Bridgewater's engineer in 1759 when the Duke obtained permission to connect his Worsley coal mines with Manchester by means of a seven-mile canal. Brindley's canal actually began inside the mine, the coal being brought out of the mine on long narrow boats called M boats; but as the ribs of these vessels were not covered by boards and so were clearly visible they were known locally as 'starvation boats'. It has been estimated that over forty miles of underground canal leads from the entrance of the Bridgewater mine. It has proved impossible to control the acid–ferruginous run-off from the system and the canal is almost always a deep orange colour, which does not seem to prevent some aquatic vegetation, three-spined sticklebacks, mallards and optimistic youngsters with nets from enjoying some aspects of what is a very colourful scene.

Apart from a canal constructed at Newry in Ireland the Bridgewater

Canal was the first 'dead water' navigation in Britain, but at the time of its construction the Sankey Brook canal, built in 1757, was already linking the St Helens coalfield with the River Mersey near Warrington. The importance of Brindley's Bridgewater Canal, however, was that it became the starting point of a network linking one part of industrial Britain with another; the building of this network reduced the cost of bulk transport, often by staggering amounts. One horse, for example, could pull a barge

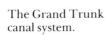

The Grand Trunk
canal system.

containing all the coal that would have been carried by sixty packhorses; by 1764 the price of coal in Manchester had been halved.

Soon a thirty-five mile extension was constructed to link with the Mersey at Runcorn, and upon its completion in 1776 the cost of carrying cotton between Liverpool and Manchester plumeted by over 85 per cent! It was small wonder that Brindley became famous within a very short period and the demands upon his time and talents became such that it seems he worked himself to death.

Britain was fast becoming the workshop of the world and raw goods pouring into the ports were diffused up the rivers and along the growing network of canals. It was at this time that many alien plants, both aquatic and terrestrial, were brought into Britain both by design and by accident, establishing themselves in the more rural areas of countryside through which the new 'cuts' slashed their way.

Following the completion of his extension to the Mersey in 1776 Brindley, fired by its dramatic success, came up with the idea of a ninety-three-mile link from the Bridgewater–Mersey end via the salt districts of Cheshire and the potteries of Staffordshire to the River Trent. The idea was to link the Mersey with the Humber so that a navigable route was made between Hull on the East Coast and Liverpool on the West. A continuous waterway of this nature certainly appealed to industrialists like Josiah Wedgwood since fragile goods could travel safely along the Trent and Mersey Canal instead of being pounded about on the back of a packhorse. The Canal Age was born.

From a natural history point of view there were now few barriers to prevent an aquatic species from extending its range by its own efforts instead of relying on natural agencies such as adhering to birds' feet or the passage of seeds through the gut of mobile animals. Even the bottoms of barges carried pieces of plant material, and any small animals adhering to these were also transported.

Some enterprises were great feats of engineering involving locking systems to raise and lower water levels artificially. Basically a lock is a stone-built basin with gates at each end. The routes through the Pennines involved the construction of a great number of locks; along the Rochdale canal, for example, there was a total of ninety-two locks in thirty-three miles. This, the first navigable water connection between Lancashire and Yorkshire, was completed in 1804. The stone locks and also bridges over canals have proved ideal habitats for the growth of ferns and other epiphytes, thus producing feeding niches for insects and also providing nesting sites for a number of birds including pied wagtails (*Motacilla alba*), robins (*Erithacus rubecula*) and wrens (*Troglodytes troglodytes*). Some of the crevices, especially along disused stretches, have shrubs such as hawthorn (*Crataegus monogyna*), elder (*Sambucus nigra*) and perhaps dogwood (*Thelycrania sanguinea*) growing out of them, and these are quickly claimed by blackbirds (*Turdus merula*), song thrushes (*Turdus philomelos*) and dunnocks (*Prunella modularis*) as nesting and feeding territories.

Canal mania continued throughout the early years of the nineteenth century and by 1830 transport 'by cut' was possible over 4,000 miles of water. The effect of such a vast network was obviously dramatic, since transport was possible against a gradient and against what little water movement there was.

Nowhere was this seen more clearly than in the case of Canadian pondweed. It is now over a hundred years since *Elodea canadensis* was introduced into Britain and, while male plants are almost unheard of in Britain, the brittle stems of the plant enable it to spread by vegetative means. Although there are no male flowers to produce pollen the minute

A horse-drawn pleasure boat on the Shropshire Union Canal. Now that commercial traffic has ceased on many waterways leisure use is increasing.   *Bill Wilkinson*

lilac female flowers still develop at the tips of long slender stalks. On a bright sunny day bubbles of oxygen can be seen issuing from the leaves, a sure sign that the Canadian pondweed is an effective photosynthesiser. This fact is well known to all students of biology, as it is used to demonstrate the process in a laboratory experiment.

In its early days the species spread so rapidly that watercourses were blocked and it was considered a positive threat to river and canal transport. Perhaps it has now used up most of some vital element, or perhaps animals have learned to use it as a food source, but for whatever reason the Canadian pondweed has now settled down to become a regular and relatively inoffensive member of our freshwater flora.

Canal transport had the dual disadvantage of being slow and of being subject to freezing during cold winters; the barges could become iced in for long periods. Then came the railway system, canal transport went out of fashion and many stretches have been left ever since to the wild things. These deserted stretches no longer receive new species but have often settled down into most interesting and integrated communities.

The initial design of canals demanded that there should be little

9

alteration in water level and thus they do not pose the same problems to aquatic life as do running waters; they do, however, have locks and thus the water does show some movement. Thus a stretch of canal can often support species typical of both ponds and slow-flowing rivers and streams.

Incorporated into canal design were a number of compensation reservoirs which quickly became favoured haunts of wildfowl and waders, regular species including mallard (*Anas platyrhynchos*), teal (*Anas crecca*), wigeon (*Anas penelope*), tufted duck (*Aythya fuligula*) and pochard (*Aythya ferina*) as well as shovellers. Waders are frequently represented by lapwings (*Vanellus vanellus*), snipe (*Gallinago gallinago*) and redshank (*Tringa totanus*). Little grebes are also happy in these conditions. The occasional rarity may also be encountered, such as the osprey (*Pandion haliaetus*) and the black tern (*Chlidonias niger*).

The reservoirs enable waterway workers to control the level and speed of waterflow along a canal, a complete contrast to both river systems and the 'drains' of the Eastern Counties, of which the Norfolk Broads are a typical example, with their rich ecological traditions now threatened by increasing pressure from pleasure craft, drainage schemes and agricultural practices.

All sorts of suggestions have been put forward to account for the origins of the Broads, a favourite idea being that they are broadened sections of rivers such as the Waveney, Yare and Bure, but with the possible exception of Breydon Water this does not seem to be the case, nor does the suggestion that they were part of a huge complex estuary with its head at a point close to the position of modern Yarmouth. This, it is suggested, became sealed off from the sea at some time following the ice ages. There is, however, no documentary evidence supporting the existence of the Broads before the fourteenth century and there is no mention of them at all in the Domesday Book. This does much to support a third, correct explanation that the Broads were formed as a result of peat digging on a large scale.

The large expanses of water formed when the peat pits were flooded by a rise in sea level are navigable and quickly attracted all forms of wildlife; at one time impressive and profitable businesses were built up based on the cutting of reeds for thatching, and by the activities of these concerns open water was maintained. In the past century the Broads have been drastically altered as a result of deliberate draining to produce land suitable for agriculture and building. The water remaining is also adversely affected by the increasing volume of holiday boat traffic.

Many of the rare plants of the shallow waters have been affected by the wash from motor boats, as a result of the activities of the introduced

Right: A flight pond on the Broadland marshes, the haunt of wildfowl and a haven for all wildlife. Many of these pieces of water, like the broads themselves, were formed by peat cutting in the Middle Ages.
Broads Authority

Below: The River Thurne and Thurne Dyke from the air. The windmills pumped water from the drainage dykes into the river; their replacement by powerful electric pumps has enabled many of the grazing marshes, once rich in both flora and fauna, to be turned into arable fields, as can be seen here.
Broads Authority

Left: Reed cutting at How Hill, Ludham. The harvesting of reeds for thatching was once a considerable industry on the Broads; the reed beds were inhabited by large numbers of birds, including the bittern.

Broads Authority

Below: Volunteer workers today play an important role in maintaining wildlife habitats on and around our rivers. These volunteers are planting water soldier (*Stratiotes aloides*) in a Broadland drainage dyke.

Broads Authority

coypu and by other factors. Increased human disturbance has also affected the breeding success of birds such as the bearded tit (*Panurus biarmicus*), bittern (*Botaurus stellaris*) and marsh harrier (*Circus aeruginosus*). Other important threats to these waters are the run-off from sewage works, which are particularly active during the holiday period, and the leaching out of agricultural fertilisers from arable fields close to the rivers. Both these enrich the water to the extent that algae grow so well that they prevent the higher plants from growing because essential light cannot reach them through the murky water. These factors added to the reduction of habitat have resulted in a very much restricted breeding range of insects such as dragonflies but especially of the swallowtail butterfly.

Conservation-minded bodies such as the R.S.P.B. have not only expressed concern but have also taken the more positive step of purchasing ecologically valuable areas. The R.S.P.B. now own Strumpshaw Broad and it will be interesting to see what positive ecological improvements take place as a result of their efforts. The Norfolk Naturalists' Trust has also been active, and apart from Hickling,

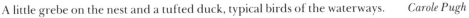

A little grebe on the nest and a tufted duck, typical birds of the waterways. *Carole Pugh*

Volunteers wiring waterlily rhizomes to engineering bricks at Barton Staithe, on the Norfolk Broads. The planting of waterlilies and other aquatic plants is one way of combating the effects of river pollution.   *Dick Flowers*

Ranworth and Cockshoot Broads which are run in conjunction with the Nature Conservancy Council the trust is active elsewhere. Its voice is felt either directly or indirectly in the running of Alderfen, Barton, Hardley Floods, Firs Marsh and Surlingham. It has even proved possible to treat over-rich waters and a pilot experiment at Cockshoot Broad in which its nine acres of water was suction-dredged sought to restore this isolated broad to its old condition; the high phosphorus levels were reduced, algae filtered out and the clarity of the water restored. A Broads Grazing Marsh Scheme under the control of the Countryside Commission, the Broads Authority and the Ministry of Agriculture, Fisheries and Food is proving successful in persuading farmers to resist the temptation to plough up their marshes and to turn them into arable fields. The lessons learnt on the Broads might well prove invaluable in the treatment of other affected rivers in the future. Rivers, canals and Broads are all used by wildlife struggling for survival and an expanding human population bent on leisure. These problems will be examined in detail in chapter ten.

Before going on to describe the various life forms it is first necessary to say something about the factors affecting all living organisms found in water. These can be classified as either physical or chemical.

Physical factors

1. Temperature

When substances are cooled they contract, and when heated they expand. This is only partly true of water, which has a unique characteristic which accounts for life under water being able to continue fairly normally even in very cold weather. As water cools it contracts, which means it becomes more dense and sinks; warmer water rises to take its place, thus producing convection currents. This circulation continues until the water temperature reaches 4°C, at which point water reaches its maximum density. Water at 3°C being less dense than that at 4°C, we have the cold layer on top and the warmer water below, an ideal arrangement for aquatic organisms living in the lower layers.

Eventually ice will form, and as this is less dense than water it will float on top, thus acting as an insulating blanket beneath which life can go on. Only very shallow water is ever likely to freeze solid, and in all but the

This diagram shows how life goes on beneath the ice in winter.

Ice
0°C
1°C
2°C
3°C
4°C

smallest ponds and ditches there will always be water beneath the ice in which fish and other creatures can live. Upper reaches of rivers are less likely to freeze over, but the slower-moving lower reaches may do so. This fact seems to be appreciated by dippers, which tend to move upstream during cold weather, a habit which initially appears illogical but which when carefully considered makes sense.

2. Water clarity

Clarity of the water is also a vital factor affecting life in water. By far the largest proportion of food available to aquatic animals comes originally from plant life, both large and small, which produces it by photosynthesis. Obviously the more transparent the water the deeper the sunlight can penetrate and the greater the volume of plant life which will be supported, and this in turn controls the number of dependent animals. The actual movement of the water can be of great importance at this point since fast-moving rivers, especially when in spate, can erode the banks and the mud and debris washed away can reduce the clarity over miles of river further downstream.

3. Buoyancy

Since water has a high density it is not necessary for organisms living in it to support their own weight. Given this support, delicate shapes and structures have evolved, and these will become apparent from descriptions of many of the aquatic flora and fauna to be described later in the book.

4. The structure of the surface film

The surface film is of vital importance to a number of highly adapted creatures. While the surface film of water does not differ in any chemical way from the layers beneath it the variation in the physical forces acting upon it produces a sort of elastic skin. The presence of this skin is easily demonstrated by lowering a darning needle on to the

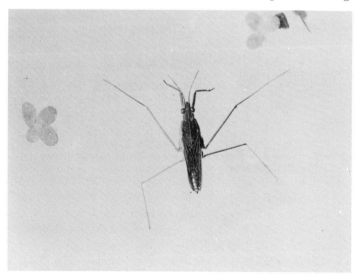

A pond skater resting on the surface film.
John Clegg

surface; if this is done carefully enough the needle will be supported by the film.

Many aquatic animals are totally dependent upon this film and if anything disrupts it such as oil, detergents, strong winds or swift currents, these creatures cannot exist for very long. The larvae of many flies hang beneath this skin, piercing it only with their breathing tubes, while others such as pond skaters walk gently along, supported by the film. While such creatures are more typical of stagnant water, they are also much in evidence in the shallows of slow-moving rivers and canals which carry a minimum of traffic. Disused canals are as stable as ponds, but areas close to functional locks are disrupted too often to support creatures totally dependent upon the surface film.

Chemical factors

The chemical constitution of each discrete area of fresh water will obviously vary and be dependent upon many factors such as underlying rock, surrounding farms and industries; even the local weather conditions will impose variations of both a temporary and a permanent nature. Some general factors will, of course, always be evident and the levels of dissolved gases such as carbon dioxide, oxygen and also to some extent nitrogen will be of importance, as will be the salts of silicon, calcium and magnesium, the latter two determining whether the water is 'hard' or 'soft'.

As we have seen, plants manufacture food from carbon dioxide and water, and so it is important that sufficient carbon dioxide is present in solution for the process to be successfully maintained. Living organisms in the water release carbon dioxide when they respire and thus recycle the gas. Oxygen required by living things for respiration is produced by plants as a by-product of photosynthesis. Providing the relative populations of plants and animals are correctly balanced the two gases will remain in equilibrium, although violent agitation of the water surface by current or by the passage of traffic can significantly increase oxygen levels.

The gas nitrogen actually makes up 78 per cent of the atmosphere and is a vital constituent of proteins, the food material essential for body growth. Although nitrogen will dissolve in water, neither plants nor animals can use it directly, with the important exception of a few vital bacteria which often live within the roots of members of the Leguminosae (pea family) and also in those of the alder. Aquatic plants obtain their nitrogen in the form of nitrates, either washed in from the land or produced as a result of the breakdown of dead plants and animals.

Animals obtain their supply of nitrogen in the form of protein which they get by eating plants or other animals.

An aquatic food chain looks something like this:

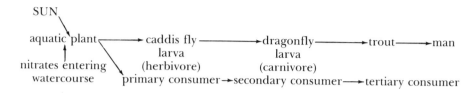

The presence or absence of certain animals, especially crustaceans and molluscs, is largely determined by whether the water is hard or soft.

The sun causes evaporation of water, leaving behind any salts dissolved in it. Eventually clouds of water vapour in the atmosphere cool and the rain falls back to the surface of the earth. During its journey through the atmosphere various gases are picked up, particularly carbon dioxide, but also sulphur dioxide and nitrogen dioxide in some industrial areas, and the resultant acidified water dissolves calcium and magnesium carbonate in the rocks to form bicarbonates; the water is then said to be hard. This type of hardness is usually referred to as temporary because it can be removed by boiling, in contrast to permanent hardness caused by sulphates and chlorides which cannot be so removed.

The effect of this weathering process is not immediately obvious, but its long-term effect can be seen in the fantastic series of caves and potholes which occur in some parts of the country. As the water gradually evaporates in these systems the solids left behind form stalactites 'growing' from the ceiling (c for ceiling and c in stalactites) and stalagmites (g for ground and in the word) 'growing' from the ground. The salts present in hard waters are extracted by molluscs and crustaceans and are essential constituents of their shells. (We also make use of these chemicals; calcium phosphate, for example, is an essential ingredient of human bone.) Areas where the rocks are not suitable for the production of hard water therefore tend to be deficient in invertebrates and are not so interesting to the natural historian, or to the angler.

Having so far considered the three main types of navigable waterways and their possible chemical constitution, we need to consider the various demands made upon them in these days of increasing recreation. It is here that there is bound to be conflict as anglers, wildfowlers, swimmers, boaters, water skiers, ornithologists and even walkers demand their share of an often diminishing habitat. Legislation

A young angler fly fishing for grayling on the River Eden near Appleby in Cumbria.
J.H. Whalley

is absolutely essential if all these demands are to be met in addition to a certain amount of extraction for domestic use.

As early as 1847 it was noticed that the discharge of waste from gasworks was harmful and the Gas Works Clauses Act came into effect in that year; in the following years a number of other acts sought to protect valuable trout and salmon fisheries, but it was not until 1898 that a scientific scale was drawn up based upon oxygen levels. Any drop below a prescribed standard was deemed unacceptable and the responsible concerns were obliged to rectify the situation. There was, and indeed still is, a problem involved when a local authority is responsible both for the pollution itself and also for the possible prosecution of the offender. It is thus faced with the problem of taking out a summons against itself.

In 1948 the River Boards Act established in England and Wales thirty-two river boards whose activities were directed towards the four important areas of land drainage, sewage disposal, water supply and

Table 1. Regional Water Authorities

Name	Area Covered
Anglian	East Suffolk, Norfolk, Essex, Great Ouse, Lincolnshire
North West	Cumbria, Lancashire, Rivers Mersey and Weaver
Northumbrian	Northumberland
Severn–Trent	Severn and Trent except for a small area of the Severn included in Wessex
Southern	Isle of Wight, Hampshire, Sussex and Kent, apart from a small area included in Thames
South West	Cornwall, Devon, and any waters entering the River Lim
Thames	Thames catchment area and the Lee catchment area, and parts of Essex and Kent which feed the Thames
Yorkshire	The whole of Yorkshire
Welsh	Dee, Clwyd, Glamorgan, Gwynedd, South-west Wales, Rivers Usk and Wye
Wessex	Avon, Dorset, Bristol, Somerset, except for part of the Avon

fisheries. Such a large number of boards was found to be unwieldy and the Water Act of 1973 pruned the authorities down to ten (see table 1). Here in addition to sewage disposal, abstraction, prevention of pollution and land drainage we find for the first time specific reference to recreation. To quote from the Act

> Every water authority and all other statutory water undertakers may take steps to secure the use of water and land associated with water for the purpose of recreation, and it shall be the duty of all such undertakers to take such steps as is reasonably practicable for putting their rights to the use of water and of any land associated with water for the use of recreation.

Recreation can require a plentiful supply of clean water and if the potentially damaging recreations of high speed boating and water ski-ing are not allowed to dominate ecologically or aesthetically valuable areas, then the balance can be very much tilted in favour of wildlife. It is on these various life forms that the rest of this book is focused.

CHAPTER TWO

The Headstream to the Middle Reaches

A S WE have seen in chapter one, early attempts to classify rivers were
made by reference to fish. In the cool, fast-flowing waters of upland
areas there is plenty of dissolved oxygen available to fish such as brown
trout, salmon, grayling and the tough little bullhead; under the stones on
the river bottom stone loaches lie hidden from the current. Many
northern rivers have their origins in upland lakes and tarns and here is
found the char, a fish with a fascinating and still not completely
understood natural history.

As the river slows down and deepens the temperature drops a little,
and although torrential conditions do sometimes occur the environment
is less demanding. Here are found the common minnow and the
uncommon barbel.

Fish of the upper reaches

Arctic char *(Salvelinus alpinus)*

A common and important food fish of the Northern Arctic, the char
is normally migratory and as it ascends rivers from the sea to spawn it is a
fine fighting fish. It is a member of the salmon family which requires
really cold water. During the period following the ice ages some char
became isolated in upland lakes in Europe, particularly Norway,
Northern Europe, the Alps and Britain.

Char in Wales, the Lake District and Scottish lochs remain in the
deep cold water but venture into the highland watercourses to spawn
during the period November to January. Unpolluted streams with stony
beds are ideal breeding grounds and acid rain (see chapter ten) must
present a threat to char in many areas, especially in Norway and Sweden,
where many river populations have already been wiped out.

The yellowish eggs measure just under 0.4 cm (0.16 inch), each
female producing up to 4,000. The young when hatched still have a large
yolk sac attached to them which is slowly absorbed over a period of
around a month, by which time the young char is already feeding on
small invertebrates, especially midge larvae (the chironomids), which are
so common in upland areas, and water fleas. The growth of the char is
slow and a twelve-year-old specimen has been known to weigh up to
10 kg (22 lb) but individuals half the size are unusual in British waters.

An Arctic char.   *John Clegg*

Specimens of 1 kg (2.20 lb) caught by patient trawling and spinner are welcome to anglers and there are few pleasanter tasting dishes than potted char. The freshly caught fish, however, look so beautiful that it seems a shame to eat them at all. The greenish back and blue-and-orange flanks spotted with delicate pink and yellow contrast beautifully with the orange-red belly. When one brings a fish to the surface shining and glistening in the sunlight one's inclination would be to throw it back if it were not for the thought of char pie.

Trout *(Salmo trutta)*

Found in all fast clear streams and rivers, the brown trout has long been popular as food and as good sport for anglers. A luxury meal not long ago, trout is now among the cheapest fish dishes as fish farms become more efficient; in 1981 more than 5,000 tons of trout were produced for market. Fish farming will be discussed in chapter ten but we are here concerned with the trout in its natural habitat of upland streams, where the fish are small but very active, requiring well oxygenated water containing sufficient minerals in solution to enable invertebrates like stoneflies and mayflies, the trout's food, to develop their exo-skeletons.

Brown trout are merely a non-migratory form of the sea trout and are recognised by their heavily spotted body, but there is an absence of spots on the tail, one feature which distinguishes them from the rainbow trout *(Salmo gairdneri)* introduced from North America and a popular fish farm species.

22

Brown trout do occur in reservoirs, but only because they have been introduced by anglers. The populations soon die out if the fish have no direct access to small streams which they require for successful spawning. Fertile fish move on to gravel beds during October to February, the 0.4 cm (0.16 inch) orange eggs taking between four and six weeks to develop, depending on temperature. Man's interference with rivers has worked against the welfare of the trout, which suffers greatly from pollution, disturbance and overfishing. Where artificial weirs have been constructed and then abandoned, an artificial trout stream is produced. On the whole, however, trout breed best on the wild uplands where young rivers are building up the strength for their journey to the sea.

Trout are usually able to breed within two or three years of hatching, by which time they are around 20 cm (8 inches) long. Even at this age

Brown trout. *Carole Pugh*

and size they can provide anglers with good sport, and trout living in rich waters such as chalk streams and lakes can be over a metre (3 feet 3 inches) long and weigh up to 8.6 kg (19 lb). The migratory sea trout, feeding on the rich pastures of the sea and moving into the rivers to breed, can reach a weight of up to 13.6 kg (30 lb) and grow to around 1.4 metres (4 feet 6 inches) long. These splendid specimens, often still

Rainbow trout. *Carole Pugh*

23

covered in sea lice, give anglers a mighty fight and have a flesh which many consider better than that of the salmon.

Salmon *(Salmo salar)*

In a booklet *Salmon conservation—a new approach* the National Water Council confirmed the feeling apparent to anglers and naturalists for many years that the salmon could be in danger of becoming extinct in British rivers. Anglers must face the fact that their overfishing is partly to blame, as is the greed of industrialists who put profits first and the environment second. Both these facts are perhaps understandable, but the real threat was laid out in the National Water Council's document:

> Illegal fishing for salmon and trout has reached 'epidemic proportions' in England and Wales. Impossible to quantify—either as to extent or effect—reliable, experienced opinion nevertheless holds that, in some areas, illegal catches regularly exceed the legal and threaten to destroy the resource.

Clearly something must be done to protect a magnificent species which was once, like oysters on the sea coast, so common that it was food for the poor and not at all valued by the rich. How things change.

Britain does, however, still have some majestic salmon rivers, especially in Scotland where Dee, Don, Tay, Tweed and Spey are all famous fisheries. In many of these rivers the demand for industrial water has meant the damming of the stream to produce reservoirs for hydro-electric schemes, cutting off the migratory fish from the spawning grounds and disrupting the breeding of salmon until artificial waterfalls called salmon ladders were built alongside the dams, up which the muscular salmon could hurl themselves. Most salmon rivers are now provided with salmon ladders; there is none finer than that at Loch Fiskally at Pitlochry in Perthshire, where an observation platform has been provided from which visitors can watch the salmon jumping. From the darkness of the viewing room one can watch fish battling against the current, illuminated by a spotlight. Each fish passing through triggers an electronic device which records the number of salmon passing upstream to the highland spawning grounds.

Few obstacles defeat the salmon's migratory urge; battered, bruised and often almost spent, they reach the breeding grounds. The breeding male with his hooked lower jaw, called a kype, lashes his tail to stimulate the gravid female to use her tail to disturb the gravel bed and form a depression in which to lay her eggs, which the male then fertilises. This exertion is often so great that the fish die as a result of their efforts; the bloated, battered bodies of the kelts, as they are called, drift downstream and rot in the shallows. The odd tough individual survives the ordeal and manages to return to the sea, revives on the rich marine food supply and returns to the river the following year to breed. A great deal of research has gone into trying to find out how salmon are able to identify the river in which they were spawned and to return to it as adults to breed. There seems no doubt, although it is difficult to prove absolutely, that young salmon learn the individual taste of their own river and are able to detect this taste even when diluted by seawater at the estuary. They then bravely follow the scent until they arrive at the breeding grounds, called redds, where they themselves were spawned.

Most eggs remain throughout the cold months before hatching during April and May. The young initially feed on the remains of the yolk sac, but by midsummer they are actively feeding on invertebrates, at which stage they are referred to as parr. They have between eight and ten bluish 'fingermarks' along the flanks, each separated by a single red

A salmon ladder on the River Wyre near Abbeysteads, typical of those provided on many salmon rivers to enable these migratory fish to reach their breeding grounds.
Ron Freethy

spot. This enables salmon parr to be distinguished from young trout, which have much less distinct fingermarks and many more red spots.

After a period of between two and five years in British waters the salmon are ready to face the journey to the sea; by this time they are between 10 and 20 cm (4–8 inches) long, and their colour has changed to silver. These smolts, as they are called, seem triggered on their migration by the rising temperatures of springtime, although they have to spend some time in estuaries until their body fluids adjust to the change in salinity and diet.

Once out to sea the salmon feeds voraciously on sand eels and young herring. The weight of this most efficient predator often increases by a staggering 3½ kilograms (over 7 lb) in its first year at sea. No wonder by the time they have spent two or three years at sea and have become sexually mature some fish have grown into monsters.

Although they do not occur in Britain there are some types of salmon, particularly in North America, that have, like our char, become land-locked, passing the whole of their life in freshwater. They are smaller than their marine relatives, a fact true of the char and also as we have seen of *Salmo trutta*.

Grayling *(Thymallus thymallus)*

When I was just beginning to wrestle with scientific names I wondered why a fish should be named after a plant; it was only when an angling friend gave me a fine plump fish to eat that I noticed that it did indeed smell just like freshly picked thyme. There surely cannot be many fish which provide their own herb flavouring.

Grayling require clear cool mountain streams, in which invertebrates

A grayling as the angler sometimes sees it.   *J. H. Whalley*

A male miller's thumb guarding and aerating the eggs.   *Michael Edwards*

such as caddisfly larvae and midge larvae are found in quantity; it will also eat fish fry, including those of its own species. Grayling have an obviously pointed head, an extended forked tail and also can be recognised by a long, tall dorsal fin; this is even larger in the male than in the female and with practice can be used to identify the sexes.

At one time the four species of grayling were classified with the salmon, but now they are placed in their own family called the Thymallidae. Only one species is found in Europe, while there are two Mongolian species and a fourth in North America.

Bullhead (*Cottus gobio*)

Also known as the miller's thumb, the bullhead can be a tough battler if the need arises, though it prefers to hide away under stones. A short sharp spine on the gill slits obviously gives some protection from enemies trying to swallow it, enemies which may well include trout. The colour varies a great deal to blend in with its background; the dorsal surface is dark and cannot be easily seen against the stream bed, while if the bullhead does venture to the surface its paler underbody is hard to see against the light. This counter-shading is seen in many animals.

27

The bullhead feeds at night, its large mouth dealing efficiently with freshwater crustaceans and insects. Bullheads are also accused by game anglers of eating the eggs of salmon, trout and grayling, but it is doubtful if bullheads do very much damage; the plump little fish, which seldom grows larger than 15 cm (6 inches), makes sure that its own eggs are well protected.

The male displays to the female, who is gravid during the period from February to April, and persuades her to lay up to a hundred sticky eggs in a depression he has scraped. This is usually under a stone, which makes it easy for him to defend during the development period of about a month. The bullhead is able to breed in its second year and may live five or six years. The fish feels very slimy to the touch, probably because bullheads do not have any scales and the skin is covered in mucus.

Stone loach *(Neomacheilus barbatulus)*

Only around 10 cm (4 inches) long, the well-camouflaged stone loach lurks on the bottom of fast-flowing streams, although also found in slower-moving stretches with muddy bottoms. Every so often the loach squirts from under a stone, which accounts for its French name of 'locher', meaning a fidget. Some workers have suggested that the stone loach is more restless when a thunderstorm is imminent; if this is the case the ability of the fish to predict a flash flood must have great survival value.

The loach has another unusual feature. It is able, if washed up on a dry bank, to gulp in air bubbles and pass them down into the intestine, where oxygen is taken into the bloodstream. The intestine therefore functions like a primitive lung, enabling the stone loach to survive for a while even if the watercourse dries up. Like the bullhead, the stone loach is also active at night, the six barbels around the mouth helping in detecting prey, which includes molluscs and invertebrates. The loach itself is eaten by trout and was taken by otters when they frequented Britain's rivers. The females are invariably larger than the males, which during the breeding season develop obvious tubercles on the skin. Yellow eggs are laid among pebbles or brookside vegetation if present and the young hatch in about two weeks, the precise period depending upon temperature.

The stone loach's narrow body varies in colour, but this does seem to depend on the background; the species has a limited ability to alter the colour as required. The yellowish blotches add to the efficient camouflage. The absence of scales and covering of mucus prevents damage as the loach scrapes between stones. In many parts of Britain it is also known as the cat-fish.

A stone loach (*Neomacheilus barbatulus*) lying almost hidden on the shingle of the river bottom.
John Clegg

Another fish found in the upper reaches of rivers, the bullhead or miller's thumb (*Cottus gobio*).
John Clegg

Familiarly disregarded as the "tiddler", the minnow (*Phoxinus phoxinus*) is by no means an insignificant part of the food chain, being eaten both by larger fish and by mammals.　*John Clegg*

The freshwater crayfish (*Astacus pallipes*) still thrives in rivers flowing through chalk and limestone, but it has been badly affected by pollution.　*John Clegg*

Minnow *(Phoxinus phoxinus)*

The minnow is one of many examples of familiarity breeding contempt. The male 'tiddler' in his breeding colours is a splendid fish, occasionally reaching a length of 12 cm (4.7 inches). Females tend, on average, to be rather larger than the males.

In breeding colours the male minnow gleams silver on the flanks, with splashes of orange and red beneath a black throat and a metallic blue on the dorsal surface. He sometimes also has white spots on the head. Although the pregnant female shows no colour changes she does become much more active in her search for stones, beneath which she lays as many as a thousand eggs which the male fertilises. Depending upon the temperature, these eggs, laid from May to mid-July, hatch between the fifth and the tenth day. Minnows feed mainly on crustaceans, but are very inquisitive fish and will be tempted towards most baits, while they themselves are eaten by larger fish and mammals such as otters, water shrews and, latterly, the mink. It is a very nutritious fish and in many parts of Europe minnows are an important part of human diet.

Barbel *(Barbus barbus)*

Preferring the upper or middle reaches of lowland rivers with a moderate current, the barbel moves slowly around the gravelly bed searching for crustaceans, insect larvae and molluscs. Only found in the south-east of Britain, it is a fine sporting fish. It is included here to make the point that not all rivers rise in high hills; the upper stretches of those rivers which flow through relatively level countryside and are never torrential form an ideal habitat for the barbel, a torpedo-shaped member of the carp family.

It is during the breeding season, beginning in May, that the barbel can really be considered as an inhabitant of the high reaches. They often undertake long journeys before the females find a suitable area of gravel in which to deposit their eggs. The smaller males are obliged to compete for the privilege of fertilising a batch of yellow eggs, which are lodged between stones, his crop of white turbercles stimulating the female to spawn.

The barbel occurs in Continental rivers, especially the Rhine. When Britain was connected to the Continent the Thames, the Nene and the Great and Yorkshire Ouse were tributaries of the Rhine and barbel were found in each. In the period following the glaciation the ice melted and rising sea levels cut off Britain from the Continent, leaving the barbel only in those rivers which had been tributaries of the Rhine.

Barbel reach an average length of 50 cm (20 inches) and a weight of 2.27 kg (5 lb), although the occasional specimen can reach 7.25 kg (16 lb).

31

Specimens of up to 90 cm (3 feet) have been recorded and they look magnificent with a green-brown dorsal surface paling to a golden yellow on the flanks and almost white on the belly. Against this background the pinkish orange paired pectoral and pelvic fins as well as the anal fin stand out clearly. The rest of the fins are darker. The real diagnostic feature, however, is the long pointed snout with four prominent barbels around the mouth, two at the front of the upper lip and two at the back of the lower. These may assist the barbel, which feeds mainly at night, to locate its food, which is mainly crustaceans and worms, although the occasional fish and some vegetation may be taken.

Invertebrates

While it is the presence of large aquatic organisms like fish which enable rivers to be classified, there are many invertebrate animals which are also typical of upland waters. Species frequently found in the early stages of rivers are crustaceans such as the crayfish and the freshwater shrimp and the larvae of insects such as stoneflies, mayflies and blackflies. How these animals are classified will be described later; in this chapter we will discuss the part they play in the overall ecology of the river.

Crayfish *(Astacus pallipes)*

Crayfish have long been important items of human food; the gourmets of the Roman Empire were very fond of this lobster-like delicacy. They must have been very common in all European rivers and

A freshwater crayfish. *Michael Edwards*

were easily caught under the stones of unpolluted streams. The poor would certainly have made use of this resource, while the rich kept crayfish in earthenware vessels and fed them a carefully controlled diet to ensure a succulent dish.

The European crayfish (*Astacus astacus*) was once economically important in France, Germany and in Scandinavia, but the population was severely reduced by a fungal parasite, *Aphanomyces astaci*, introduced in imported crayfish from America. Crayfish, which are dark brown in colour, require limestone in order to develop the protective shell; the acid rain now falling on Scandinavia has destroyed this hard water, resulting in a population crash.

Pollution in British waters has substantially reduced the population of *Astacus pallipes* but they still thrive in the hard waters flowing through chalk and limestone areas. Measuring up to 16 cm (6½ inches) long, the crayfish is mainly nocturnal and is a true scavenger, feeding on vegetation and animals alive or dead. It is also quite partial to other crayfish, especially when they are helpless at the time they are moulting.

The head and thorax are fused together to form a cephalothorax, and it is only when the creature is turned over that the animal's abdomen is revealed. This is obviously segmented, and the body ends with a tail fin known as the telson. Each segment has a pair of limbs which not only serve to propel the animal through the water and along the river bed but also have gills at their bases. These are rich in haemoglobin, which absorbs oxygen from the water to provide the rich oxygen supply on which the crayfish depends. The predatory crayfish is very heavy and it takes a great deal of energy to move quickly, which is why it is so dependent upon an abundant supply of oxygen.

During mating the male, which is usually larger than the female, turns the female on to her back and squirts a sticky seminal fluid on to her abdomen; the first pair of limbs on his abdomen have become modified into a tube for this purpose. The female then returns to the dark confines of her burrow in the river bank below water level, where she produces more than a hundred eggs which she secures to the hair-like structures on her swimming legs, called swimmerets, fertilising them with the sperms adhering to her abdomen. She transfers the fertilised eggs to grooves on her abdomen, and thus can carry them around with her. In this condition she is said to be 'in berry'.

The eggs are produced as late as November and hatch out the following spring, the young still remaining attached to the female for a period, usually until after the first moult when they become independent. Their efficient feeding depends upon the development of the chelipeds or pincers, which are formidable weapons. The crayfish goes through a series of moults as it grows into an adult. After they are sexually mature, usually in their fourth year, crayfish moult only once a year. They usually consume their old shells, a sensible recycling of scarce resources. During this period the crayfish is very vulnerable to predators; it may well be that the availability of suitable hiding places is just as important in its distribution as the presence of swift-moving, well-oxygenated water.

Freshwater shrimp *(Gammarus pulex)*

Freshwater shrimps are found in a great many habitats. Those in the genus *Gammarus* are very active little creatures and have high oxygen demands. This requirement for a good supply of oxygen, coupled with the need to produce tough exoskeletons, tends to restrict them to fairly hard and fast-flowing waters, a habitat they share with the crayfish.

Gammarus is very easy to recognise because it swims on its side. Many specimens will be found by turning over stones in shallow water. Their food being mainly dead animal and plant material, shrimps serve a useful function in cleaning river and stream beds of debris. *Gammarus* itself is eaten by crayfish, trout and other fish as well as by birds such as the dipper. Thus are the complex feeding webs constructed.

Gammarus breeds throughout the year, the male clasping the female who releases her eggs into an open-ended tube formed by the second and fourth thoracic segments being folded over the ventral surface. The number of eggs varies, probably depending upon the availability of food, from under fifty to over a thousand. The period of development is considerably shorter during the summer than in winter, but ten moults are required before the animal itself can breed. At times huge populations can build up very quickly and it is no wonder that *Gammarus* is so important in the diet of higher animals. Also important in this respect are the larvae of stoneflies, mayflies and blackflies.

Stonefly larvae (Plecoptera)

The majority of the stonefly species have larvae preferring fast-running watercourses, the same applying to the larvae of the mayflies (Ephemeroptera). They can easily be distinguished by the fact that stonefly larvae have tails made up of two prongs, whereas those of mayflies have three such structures. Care should be taken, however, to refer to the correct keys as the occasional mayfly is found with only two tails (see bibliography).

Adult stoneflies, which are dull brown in colour, are never found very far from water. They have two long tails and a pair of very long antennae. There are two similar pairs of wings, but in many males they are so small as to be almost useless. Even females which need to fly in order to disperse the species are not very efficient aeronauts. Adult stoneflies take a little solid food in the form of algae and lichens, but they do not grow and therefore usually require only liquids to sustain them until the eggs have been laid.

The adults tend to remain hidden on the underside of leaves, especially alder, emerging only to breed. After a brief mating the female drops bundles of eggs into the water, and these hatch into nymphs some six to nine weeks later, the precise time depending upon the temperature. This is the most important factor. Each female can produce up to two thousand eggs. There are some thirty-four species of stoneflies present in Britain, classified into seven families.

The period spent as a nymph varies, but it is never less than a year and sometimes as long as three. The nymphs are not good swimmers, but their flat bodies hold strongly to the stones. Some species are vegetarians and graze on the algae growing on the stones, others need to hunt for small worms and may even resort to cannibalism, especially if they come across another stonefly nymph while it is moulting and therefore defenceless.

The stage of development of the nymph can be estimated by looking for signs of wing buds. These appear after a number of moults and gradually enlarge until the stoneflies leave the water for their brief nuptial flight. This is when the trout rise to snap up a juicy morsel. The adult stonefly can have a wing span of 5 cm (2½ inches). Anglers know stonefly larvae as 'creepers' because of their slow, deliberate movement over the stream bed, but they invariably confuse the adults and group them together as mayflies.

Mayflies (Ephemeroptera)

Anglers know the emerging adult mayfly well, call it a spinner, and know what a fatal lure it is to a hungry trout. Just before the adult emerges and before the wings are filled with air the duller insect is known as a 'dun'.

There are eight families of mayflies found in British waters, the precise number of species varying from forty-six to fifty depending upon the authority consulted. They are never found very far away from water and while some forms such as *Cloeon* prefer slow-moving water, other species such as *Ecdyonurus* have very light and flattened larvae which cling tightly to stones and can exist in fast-running streams. They run with a sideways motion rather resembling crabs, preferring not to swim.

The insect's adult stage may last only a few minutes, and it seldom survives longer than a couple of days; thus do the mayflies earn their

35

name of Ephemeroptera. The mouth parts are so degenerate that feeding is impossible, and once the meagre food reserves within the body are used up the insects die. Their legs will allow adult mayflies to perch but not to move. They tend to remain hidden until dusk and then to fly around in nuptial swarms during which the female is roughly seized by the male; mating occurs as the two spiral downwards. The male invariably dies immediately after mating while the female flies low over the water laying anything from one thousand to four thousand eggs.

Some larvae complete their metamorphosis in a year, but other species take two years or even longer. In the early stages the larva breaks through the cuticle which covers the body; tracheal gills develop after the first couple of months; these can be seen working when mayfly nymphs are examined after removal from the cool oxygen-rich water, the rate of gill vibration rising quickly as oxygen supplies diminish. On the whole mayfly larvae are vegetarians, but some animal matter is occasionally taken.

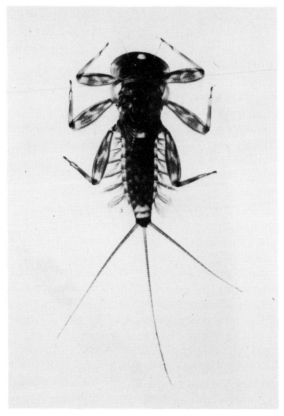

The flattened larva of a mayfly (*Ecydonurus*), found in fast-flowing streams. *John Clegg*

Eventually the nymphs develop wing buds and then air begins to collect between two layers of cuticle, the buoyant insect being carried to the surface. The emergence of the adult takes place quickly; speed is essential if mayfly are to survive in waters full of hungry fish.

Blackflies (Simuliidae)

Blackflies are seldom recognised but frequently felt by those of us who enjoy watching aquatic life. Female Simuliidae feed on human blood, and to obtain this they inflict an often very painful bite. The predominant colour of the adults, which are only 2.5 mm (0.1 inch) long, is grey but they can be recognised by having antennae just a little longer than the head. The wings also bear a very distinct vein near to the border.

After mating the female emerges from the huge swarm of 'midges' and lays her eggs by the side of the water near enough to be splashed but not swamped. The larva is segmented and shows a fascinating method of respiration in which gills emerge from the anus, which opens on the eighth segment. It bears a tail attachment often consisting of a series of hooks, while the head end carries a brush-like structure which sweeps food towards the mandibles. The head also bears primitive eyes and a pair of antennae. The larva can live in water for as long as six months, during which time it can grow to a maximum size of almost 2.5 cm (1 inch). The larva then pupates inside a tough brown cocoon which is attached either to a stone or to the stem of an aquatic plant.

After about three weeks the pupa case absorbs air from the water and bobs to the surface like a cork. The adult emerges quickly and joins the vast clouds of midges which are such a rich food supply for visiting swallows, house martins and sand martins.

Birds

Dipper *(Cinclus cinclus)* and grey wagtail *(Motacilla cinerea)*

Tumbling waterfalls and steep wooded gorges hanging with spray make the naturalist's visit to the uplands memorable, especially when dippers and grey wagtails are searching for invertebrates under stones.

At first glance it would seem that the two species are in direct competition for food, but a period of quiet observation shows how subtle is nature's way of providing for all. The dipper walks into the stream, submerges and walks on the stony bed, turning stones and filling its bill with mayfly, stonefly and *Simulium* larvae. The grey wagtail on the other hand chooses to feed in the shallows, using its long tail as a balancing organ as it moves from one slippery stone to the next. Thus each bird avoids competition with the other by each having what scientists call its unique ecological niche. In the gentler meanders further downstream the grey wagtail may find itself ousted by the pied wagtail (*Motacilla alba*), and therefore the former tends to be restricted to the more turbulent areas, providing further proof that every bird has its place.

The theory of the ecological niche goes far beyond this one simple example; it can be shown that no two living organisms can occupy the same habitat and feed on the same food supply without one being slightly more efficient than the other. Gradually the fitter species will out-breed the less efficient, and the latter will eventually become extinct or adapt to another habitat.

Grey and pied wagtail.   *Carole Pugh*

Returning to the wagtails, there is a further niche where the meandering river eases gently through lush green meadows, which tend to flood and freeze in winter. This habitat is used by the summer-visiting yellow wagtail (*Motacilla flava*), which occupies this niche without any interference from either the pied or the grey wagtail.

CHAPTER THREE

The Middle Reaches

THE AREA most likely to conjure up in the mind a picture of a typical river is the middle reaches, overhung with trees and rippling through a sunlit countryside. Once the fierce upland waters have slowed, the current is much more easily tamed, and it was in the middle reaches that early human settlements developed and that first stepping stones and then bridges spanned the shallower areas. Fords would have been important crossing points along the green roads; drovers would have used them as they took their stock to markets, often far from their homes.

Prior to the Industrial Revolution the rich fertile fields lying alongside the lazy meanderings of rivers were full of flowers and the summer air vibrated to the tune of buzzing insects. The moderate runoff of excrement from farms added to the fertility of many rivers until comparatively recent times, when artificial fertilisers were introduced in an effort to increase efficiency. The pursuit of profits also meant the initially indiscriminate use of pesticides and herbicides, which were flushed by rain into rivers with disastrous effects upon aquatic wildlife. At the same time the drive towards agricultural efficiency and the growth of industrial towns as well as the human population meant that vast areas of marginal land were drained for building or farming, the rivers being used as open sewers. The first organisms to suffer as a result of these changes were those living in ditches, which were often tributaries feeding into the middle reaches of rivers.

The otter (*Lutra lutra*) once found this habitat ideal, but increased drainage, pollution and hunting pressure have greatly reduced its population. Other species still occur in high numbers.

Mammals of ditches

Harvest mouse (*Micromys minutus*)

One mammal which is often surprisingly common around ditches is the harvest mouse. Its lightness, its supple agility and its ability to use its tail as a prehensile limb enable the harvest mouse to climb reeds and to feed and even to breed high above water level. This was almost certainly the original habitat of the species before cereal crops began to be grown on a large scale. In recent years a census has been taken of the harvest mouse during the autumn when it is possible to count the nests without disturbing breeding. The harvest mouse has been found to be more common and also much more widely distributed, especially in northern England, than was previously suspected. It has even been found in several sites in Scotland, where its presence had not been suspected.

Harvest mice have been found to construct two types of nest, one used as a breeding site and around 10 cm (4 inches) in diameter; the other type is used only as shelter and is about half the size. The breeding nests are often snugly lined with thistledown. Watching Britain's smallest mammal, weighing only about 8 gm (0.28 oz) and measuring less than

A harvest mouse clambering along the stems of riverside vegetation. *Will Bown*

15 cm (6 inches) from nose to tail, sway about on a reed as it skilfully plaits its nest by shredding reeds is one of the most marvellous sights in nature.

The breeding season can begin as early as March and continue until September. Food stores are laid up for the winter and the dainty little beast is far less delicate than it seems. A litter of up to seven is born after a gestation period of twenty-one days; the babies open their eyes after a week and are suckled for about a fortnight. They can breed themselves at six weeks, which means that large populations can build up very quickly, but harvest mice are not long lived, many dying in the first year, with only the occasional animal surviving for as long as three years.

Water vole *(Arvicola terrestris)*

Despite its rather misleading Latin name the water vole swims with great vigour and is often called the 'water rat', despite having an attractive hamster-like face. The diet of the animal is mainly riverside vegetation, but there are a few records of it occasionally eating carrion. I once watched a water vole feeding on a kelt salmon in such an advanced state of decay that it would have been anything but a wholesome meal by human standards.

Breeding usually begins around April and may continue into September; during this time no more than two litters of four or five young will be produced by each female. Because of this, populations do not build up quickly, but water voles, which measure 32 cm (nearly 13 inches) from nose to tail and weigh 250 gm (28.4 gm equals 1 oz), can live for up to five years. On balance they do little damage apart from the occasional undermining of river banks. This damage is slight compared to that perpetrated by a South American import, the coypu.

Bank vole *(Clethrionomys glareolus)*

It is not surprising to find water voles common in ditches rich in succulent vegetation, but the bank vole is perhaps unexpected in such an environment. It is, however, often abundant in the upper and drier areas of ditches, especially if their crests are planted with hawthorn, pollarded willows or other shrubs.

Less than half the size of the water vole and with a comparatively shorter tail, the bank vole can be mistaken for the field vole *(Microtus agrestis)* but its pelage is much redder. Neither the water vole nor the bank vole is native to the Isle of Man or Ireland, although a recent attempt to introduce the latter into Ireland appears to have been successful. The molar teeth of the bank vole are semi-rooted and are not able to cope with the really tough vegetation which the field vole relishes; this may be the reason why bank voles frequent damp areas in woods and alongside ditches where the succulent aquatic vegetation is easy on the teeth.

Birds of ditches

The heron *(Ardea cinerea)* and the kingfisher *(Alcedo atthis)* are well-known birds frequenting ditches and low-lying areas around rivers and both will be described in chapter eight. Little grebes, water rails and a number of fascinating warblers are common in such places as the rhynes of the Somerset Levels and the dykes which abound in the Norfolk Broads.

Little grebe *(Tachybaptus ruficollis)*

More often heard than seen, the little grebe or dabchick is a wary little bird. Its chattering contact call bubbling out of the reeds is often the only evidence of its presence. Its dumpy body is around 27 cm (11 inches). As soon as danger threatens it slips quietly under water, its passing causing no more than a gentle ripple. Little grebes are able to dive to depths of around 2 metres (6 feet 6 inches), though they prefer the water to be shallower than this, and feed on insect larvae, crustaceans, molluscs, young amphibians and the occasional small fish.

Water rail *(Rallus aquaticus)*

If the little grebe is considered shy, then the water rail must be the master recluse, its high-pitched squeak being usually the only clue the ornithologist gets to its presence deep within the reed cover. In the depths of a hard winter, with its food supply frozen solid, the starving rail must sally forth from cover, and it is only then that the true population of these birds can be realised. In fact the breeding population in Britain may be approaching 4,000 pairs, just under half that of the little grebe. Water rails prefer animal food, including crustaceans and aquatic insects as well as fish, but they will take vegetable matter on occasions, especially, it seems to me, during cold spells.

Warblers

The warblers were once described to me by an old man of the marshes who made his living cutting osiers as 'little brown things'. How right he was, for they are certainly difficult to identify one from the other. Four species of particular interest to the ditch watcher are the reed warbler *(Acrocephalus scirpaceus)*, marsh warbler *(Acrocephalus palustris)*, sedge warbler *(Acrocephalus schoenobaenus)* and the increasing Cetti's warbler *(Cettia cetti)*.

The reed warbler is about 12.5 cm (5 inches) long and is recognised by its reddish rump contrasting with the duller brown on the back. The long bill and the warbling song are also diagnostic. The nest is slung between reeds, which makes it particularly vulnerable in stormy weather when the swaying of the reeds disturbs the nest. The clutch of four or five eggs is incubated by both sexes; they start to sit before the clutch is complete, which means that not all the young hatch together, with the result that the eldest chick is stronger than the others. If there is a shortage of food the strongest gets all the food, thus ensuring its survival. This asynchronous hatching is typical of birds of prey but is most unusual in passerine species such as the summer visiting warblers.

There are probably more than 70,000 pairs of reed warblers

breeding in Britain compared with fewer than a hundred pairs of marsh warblers. This species can be confused with the reed warbler, but the bill is shorter and thicker, the throat decidedly paler, and the dorsal plumage is not red. The distinction is, however, not easily made; further confusion is caused by the fact that the male is a superb mimic and can copy the songs of other species, including the reed warbler.

The rare marsh warbler is restricted to southern Britain, especially Worcestershire, where males are to be found singing from a song post above the patch of nettles in which the nest is sited. Under Schedule 1 of the Protection of Birds Act, 1954 to 1967, the marsh warbler may not be interfered with by anyone without a licence and it will remain a rare visitor.

This rarity label certainly cannot be applied to the sedge warbler, of which over 300,000 breeding pairs are to be found distributed throughout the whole of the British Isles. Sedge warblers, which arrive in Britain during April, are recognised by their prominent white eye stripe which stands out clearly against the dark crown of the head. During the summer they weigh around 12 grams (under 0.5 oz) but just before migration they store sub-cutaneous fat which can double the body weight. Their migratory journey is usually accomplished in one continual flight, but some drastic decrease in numbers has occurred in recent years because the Sahel region of Africa, the birds' first stopping place, has been suffering from a drought. The same fate has befallen the whitethroat (*Sylvia communis*) which also depends upon the Sahel for water. The weather has relented somewhat recently and the population of both species is recovering.

Savi's warbler once nested commonly in the Fen districts but was extinct by 1856. In 1973 the birds returned to the reed beds of south-eastern England, but there are still fewer than twenty pairs, which are, of course, fully protected. The re-establishment of this 14 cm (5½ inches) buff-coloured warbler with round tail and buzzing song is just one important reason—among many others—why ditches and damp areas around rivers should be fiercely protected.

Amphibians of ditches

At one time Britain's extensive marshes must have reverberated to the sound of croaking frogs and toads, while newts must have inhabited every puddle, pool, ditch and slow-moving river. The great crested newt (*Triturus cristatus*) urgently needs extra protection if it is not to become extinct and the range of the palmated newt (*Triturus helveticus*) is also shrinking alarmingly in many countries. Only the well-named smooth or

A male crested newt. *Carole Pugh*

common newt (*Triturus vulgaris*) can be considered safe, and along with the common toad (*Bufo bufo*) is to be found in and around most ditches and slow-moving rivers. The common frog (*Rana temporaria*) has not proved to be quite as resilient as either *Bufo bufo* or *Triturus vulgaris* and is in urgent need of protection in many areas.

Left: A male palmate newt.
E. C. M. Haes

Opposite: Three-spined sticklebacks. *John Clegg*

Fish of ditches

When ditches lead directly into rivers fish of the slow-moving stretches may well venture into them, especially during periods of rain, and species such as three-spined sticklebacks (*Gasterosteus aculeatus*) may well thrive here permanently. When as a child I was once paddling in a ditch I was terrified to see an eel emerge from the water, slither over the mud and disappear into the damp grass. I had no doubt that I had seen a snake, but I know now that here was an eel (*Anguilla anguilla*) with an urge to breed, heading for the sea. Despite their familiarity, both the stickleback and the eel have a biology every bit as fascinating as, and perhaps more fascinating than, any other fish.

Stickleback (*Gasterosteus aculeatus*)

Easily recognised by the three long spines projecting from its back, the 'tiddler' of the park lake is one of Britain's most unusual and beautiful fish. An average sized specimen is around 5 cm (2 inches) long, the occasional specimen reaching twice this size.

Two aspects of its behaviour set the stickleback apart from other fish. Firstly it is found both in small ponds and also as far as five miles out to sea, the stickleback seeming able very quickly to adjust its body fluids from the freshwater habitat to the marine, a delicately balanced process which takes both the salmon and the eel a great deal longer. Secondly the brilliantly flashing blue eyes and scarlet throats of the males attract the females and persuade them to lay up to 400 eggs in a nest which the male has made of weed stuck together with secretions from his kidneys. Nests

are built both in freshwater and marine habitats, another unusual feature.

The male aerates the eggs, which hatch in one to three weeks depending upon temperature, by directing a current of water through the nest with his fins, and he is most courageous in defence of his nest. I once watched a brave stickleback attacking a Coca-cola tin which had been thrown into a slow-moving river by a picnicker; he only ceased his buffeting when I removed the can. Sticklebacks are sometimes sexually mature in their first year, but just as often they are two years old before they breed. They seldom survive beyond their third year, which is not surprising when one considers the formidable list of predators lined up against them, including the eel.

Eel *(Anguilla anguilla)*

Even by science fiction standards the life history of an eel follows a surprising sequence, and it says much for the tenacity of naturalists that the details have been unravelled at all. The salmon breeds in freshwater but migrates to the sea to feed, a piece of behaviour referred to as anadromous. The eel breeds in the sea and visits the land during the 'adolescent' period, behaviour which is said to be catadromous. The eel is thus a marine species. There are many details of the eel's life cycle which are still not fully understood.

Eels of the species *Anguilla anguilla* are found throughout Europe and North Africa but all make a journey of between 4,000 km and 7,000 km (2,500 miles–4,375 miles) to the Sargasso sea in the middle regions of the mighty Atlantic to breed. The tiny almost-transparent larvae, called leptocephali, are flattened creatures only 5 mm long (0.2 inches); they have been found at depths of 300 metres but they visit the surface to feed on diatoms, which are tiny algae, and thus play their part in the food chains of the oceans. By the time they have drifted in the ocean currents for three years the little eels are ready to metamorphose into elvers, having reached a size of around 70 mm (2.8 inches). They are now ready to enter the estuaries and, after a period of adjustment, to move up rivers and occasionally through damp grass until they reach a suitable habitat. On the west coast of Britain elvers move up rivers during January to March, but east coast rivers do not have their elver run until March or April. This migration was well known to the old-time eel catchers, who sold the succulent creatures to customers who knew a variety of recipes by which the eel could be turned into a most tempting dish.

During their period of development in fresh water, which can take as long as ten years but does depend upon food supply and temperature,

Totridge Fell frowns down on the placid River Hodder in Lancashire.	*Michael Edwards*

The bright colouring of the male stickleback attracts the more sombrely coloured female.

John Clegg

The swallowtail butterfly (*Papilio machaon*) is now confined to the Norfolk Broads; it was formerly found along many English rivers.

Robert Howe

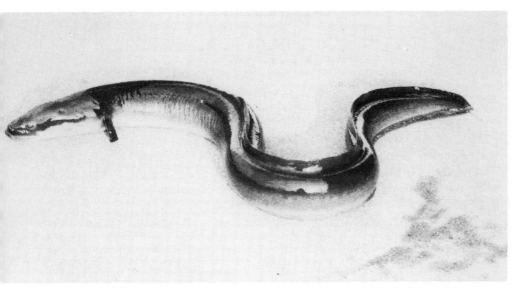

The eel is a fish which breeds in the sea and comes upriver during its adolescent period, at which time it feeds on fish and their eggs, crustaceans, insects, molluscs and worms.

Ron Freethy

eels feed on fish and their eggs, which makes them hated by anglers, as well as upon crayfish and smaller crustaceans, insects, molluscs and worms. During this phase eels are yellow in colour, but as they become sexually mature the back darkens and the belly becomes silvery. Thus we have 'yellow' and 'silver eels'. Females can grow up to 1 metre (39.4 inches) and weigh up to 12.7 kg (28 lb) but few specimens reach this size; the males are approximately half these measurements. As the eels reach the 'silver' stage they cease to feed and, following the reproductive urge, overcome all obstacles until they reach the Sargasso breeding grounds, where they spawn and die.

Invertebrates of ditches

Standing by a ditch, with skylarks singing overhead and reed buntings wheezing their calls from the tall vegetation, the naturalist should not resist the urge to sit down. In such spots many years ago swallowtail butterflies were common but these beautiful insects have sadly declined; here too were the hated leeches and the beloved jewels of the marshlands, the sparkling dragonflies.

Swallowtail butterfly *(Papilio machaon)*

Now only breeding in the Norfolk Broads area, the swallowtail has disappeared from many of its former haunts because of the loss of marshland habitat and the disappearance of its principal larval food plant, the milk parsley *(Peucedanum palustre)*, due to the over-zealous use of herbicides (see chapter four). Occasionally the larvae will feed on fennel *(Foeniculum vulgare)*, wild angelica *(Angelica sylvestris)* and wild carrot *(Daucus carota)*.

The point is often made that as the swallowtail is a strong flier and often reaches Britain on migration from the Continent we should not worry too much if it becomes extinct in Britain. On the Continent, however, the species frequents a wider range of habitats, including much higher, drier ground. The British swallowtail is, in fact, separated as a sub-species, *Papilio machaon britannicus*, and is recognised by its darker appearance due to wider black bands on the wings. The male can easily be distinguished from the female by his pair of anal claspers and by his more angular wings, which are also decorated by yellow triangular plates. Breeding occurs during May and June and the mainly green caterpillar, banded with black and blotched with red and black, feeds during the summer. It is the pupa which overwinters; it is surprisingly tough, being able not only to withstand all weathers but even to survive flooding.

Medicinal leech *(Hirudo medicinalis)*

An interesting species of leech which used to be found in large numbers in our ditches is the medicinal leech, an invaluable item of commerce for centuries. The young leeches feed on invertebrates. It was

The medicinal leech, which still has a use in hospitals, is recognised by its yellowish green ventral surface, covered with black spots.
John Clegg

thought for many years that the adults were unable to survive unless they had fed upon mammalian blood, but this is now known to be untrue; the leeches' love of human blood made them popular in the days when 'bleeding' was thought to be sensible treatment. They are used today to remove clottted blood from patients, especially after eye operations, when the risk of thrombosis is high.

This species is recognised by its yellowish green ventral surface which is covered with black spots. The back is somewhat darker green but with six brownish bands across it, and there are also a number of black spots. This is a large leech and can reach lengths of 15 cm (6 inches). Leeches will be more fully discussed in chapter five.

Dragonflies

One of the most aggressive species (see chapter seven) is the brown aeshna, also known as the brown hawker (*Aeshna grandis*. It is a very strong flier and is strongly territorial, patrolling a regular beat and

The brown aeshna.
Carole Pugh

catching insects on the wing. The brown hawker is still common in the south-east but tends to be less common in the north and is absent from almost all of Scotland.

Wet meadows and the river meander

As rivers slow down the bed becomes more stable, the surface becomes less disturbed and the deeper layers are warmer, factors which combine to ensure a rich vegetation. Kingfishers thrive here along ditches, and sand martins (*Riparia riparia*) find the more stable banks much to their liking. Little grebes also thrive here, as do mallard (*Anas platyrhynchos*), moorhens (*Gallinula chloropus*), coot (*Fulica atra*) and the mute swan (*Cygnus olor*). These and other riverside birds will be dealt with fully in chapter eight.

The wet meadows next to the meanders are an ideal habitat for other

51

species, some of which, like the black tern (*Chlidonias niger*) and the black-tailed godwit (*Limosa limosa*), are very rare. If the latter species, which returned to breed on the Ouse washes on the borders of Norfolk and Cambridgeshire around 1952, is to survive and perhaps increase it is essential that these wetland habitats are preserved. Bodies such as the

A moorhen on the nest and, below, a coot.   *Carole Pugh*

Royal Society for the Protection of Birds (R.S.P.B.) have spent a great deal of money on the purchase and upkeep of threatened wetland sites, and it is hard to think of money better spent. In addition to rarities, reserves established on wetlands are attractive to breeding redshank (*Tringa totanus*) and the snipe (*Gallinago gallinago*). It is the plants of meadows which are the real joy, however, and these will be described in chapter four.

Invertebrates of the meanders

As the river flows gently in its sinuous curves oxbows are produced as well as sheltered backwaters where conditions are much like a pond and the surface film is seldom ruptured. Here such species as water fleas, whirligig beetles and caddisflies can be found and fish such as chub and bream are at the top of the food chain.

Water fleas

There are many species of water flea, tiny crustaceans typical of fresh water which move in a series of sudden jerks, from which habit they get their name. The body is enclosed in a sort of protective jacket called the carapace, so transparent that through it the heart can be seen beating. Food, mainly diatoms, can be seen working its way through the gut. Perhaps the best known family is Daphnidae, to which the most common species, *Daphnia pulex*, belongs.

Whirligig beetles (Gyrinidae)

How well this family earns both its vernacular and scientific names as it twists and gyrates on the water; this movement disturbs its food and makes it easier to catch. Both animal and vegetable food is taken, the vortex created by the giratory movement drawing up edible items towards the beetle, which is ideally adapted for living on the surface film. Rapidly moving water is not suitable for whirligigs. Even their eyes have bifocal lenses to enable *Gyrinus* species to see both above and below the surface.

Caddisflies

The adult caddisflies, dull coloured and fluttering feebly among the fringing vegetation, are often and understandably confused with moths; it is the larval forms which are so well known to pond and river biased naturalists.

After the female has laid her eggs they absorb water and swell rather like a mass of frog spawn. These swollen eggs are usually found in flat masses or even in circles, which when picked up in a net and released in a jar of water look rather like smoke rings. The resultant larvae soon make a protective case of stones or vegetation in which to live. Some species do not build a case but spread a net almost like a spider's web between the stones of upland streams, feeding on small animals trapped in the meshes. Most caddis larvae are vegetarians, however; they move slowly through still or slow-moving waters grazing on vegetation.

Not being very active, caddisflies can live in water somewhat deficient in oxygen, but they do have tube-shaped gills on the abdomen. The last segment bears jointed appendages, each terminating in a hook which is used to grip the case and thus resist the forcible removal of the larva. The classification of caddisflies will be briefly covered in chapter six.

Fish

Chub *(Leuciscus cephalus)* **and bream** *(Abramis brama)*

The chub typifies the middle reaches of the river, while the bream is said by many Continental workers to be typical of the lower reaches just before the river enters its estuary.

The chub can reach an average size of 36 cm (14.2 inches) and weigh 700 gm (24.7 oz). Although very bony and not usually eaten, the chub is a

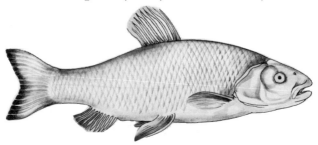

Chub.   *Carole Pugh*

fighting fish much loved by anglers, who fish for it with both fly and spinner. Shoals of chub are found near the surface although the larger specimens, often 60 cm long (23.6 inches) and up to 4 kg (nearly 9 lb), tend to be solitary. In winter all chub seek out the deeper water, although they return to shallow water to spawn. Males can breed during their third year, but females are four or even five before they spawn for the first time.

Bream are usually about the same length as chub, but the plate-like body can weigh up to 9 kg (19.8 lb) and is much fuller than that of the chub. The bream is eagerly sought as a food fish in parts of Europe; they are easily transported and can breathe for some time out of water and so are popular with anglers wishing to stock fisheries. It is likely that they could be farmed for food in future (see chapter eleven).

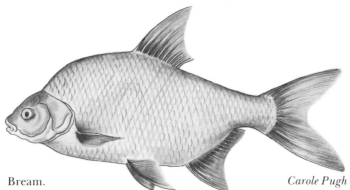

Bream.   *Carole Pugh*

CHAPTER FOUR

The Lower Reaches and Estuary

As THE river approaches the sea its current slows down, its channel becomes wider and there is a gradual increase in salinity.

When the fresh water carrying a rich load of solid particles by virtue of its high velocity meets the incoming sea with its own supply of flotsam and jetsam, there is produced an area of still water where the two cancel each other out. The material being carried by the two currents sinks to produce a nutrient-rich silt which fuels the food chains so typical of estuaries.

With the exception of the three-spined stickleback few organisms can survive the sudden change from fresh to salt water, most requiring a period of temporary residence in the estuary. In this respect the area provides what can be regarded as the equivalent of a diver's decompression chamber, allowing a period of gradual adjustment rather than a sudden change.

Both the eel and the salmon, whose biology has already been discussed, require a period of adjustment in the estuary before continuing their journey to the breeding grounds. This is also true of the sturgeon (*Acipenser sturio*), which is a bottom-living fish feeding and growing in the sea but spawning in deep rivers having a strong current. The roe of the female is sold as caviar; as many as two million eggs can be produced by a single female, but over-exploitation has reduced the sturgeon's numbers to the point at which there is now only one important fishery in the Black Sea, although the very occasional specimen still turns up in British waters. Sturgeon can live as long as ten years and specimens can weigh up to 400 kg (882 lb).

Flounders (*Platichthys flesus*), normally marine fish, often move far upstream, especially if there is little pollution, and they are now found in the Thames as far as Central London. Wheeler also reported the plaice (*Pleuronectes platessa*) as far up the Thames as the area around the Dartford Tunnel, while the dab (*Limanda limanda*) and the sole (*Solacea solea*) are other flat fish now finding Thames river water acceptable. The herring (*Clupea harengus*) was also reported by Wheeler to be regularly seen around the Blackwall Tunnel area. It is small wonder that seals, especially the common (*Phoca vitulina*), often pursue these sea fish through the estuary and are reported under the bridges of towns where their natural inquisitiveness makes them look up at passing traffic and at equally inquisitive human faces.

Unfortunately there are often too many human faces and far too much activity around our estuaries for the wildlife living in them and around them to thrive. All Britain's large estuaries have been subject to industrial development and most bristle with oil refineries, chemical plants, shipbuilding yards and, latterly, nuclear power stations. Few estuaries have been left undisturbed; but Morecambe Bay, a complex estuary on the boundary of Lancashire and Cumbria draining several rivers including the Lune, Kent, Keir and Leven, has remained relatively untouched. A recently built nuclear power station at Heysham and massive installations to cope with oil and offshore gas now bring the Bay under threat.

From time to time the suggestion is made that barrages should be constructed across not only Morecambe Bay but across the Dee and Duddon estuaries and also the Wash and the Severn. Would we not be better advised to conserve what water supplies we have already rather than threaten our estuaries even more than we have in the past? We should not forget that many of our seaside resorts are close to estuaries and that holidaymakers bring their own threat to wildlife. Caravan sites and car parks have been constructed by flattening sand dunes, once the home of rare amphibians such as the natterjack toad (*Bufo calamita*) and sand lizard (*Lacerta agilis*), while the physical presence of innocent

Natterjack toad.   *Carole Pugh*

strollers, swimmers or beach anglers can disturb breeding birds such as ringed plovers (*Charadrius hiaticula*), oyster catchers (*Haematopus ostralegus*) and terns, especially the little tern (*Sterna albifrons*).

Conservationists are rightly concerned when they see estuarine life destroyed by what they regard as human interference, but a much

Little tern. *Carole Pugh*

greater threat to some of our remaining estuaries still rich in wildlife is posed by what amounts to Nature's own supergrass—*Spartina*. While argument rages on about acid rain, intrusions into green belts and the theft of the eggs of rare birds, spartina the supergrass has been silently strangling our estuaries. Spartina arrived at Southampton on board ship from America and soon grew strongly on the mudflats near Hythe. Since then it has swamped many areas which were once important feeding areas for wildfowl and waders, preventing the growth of normal salt marsh plants such as sea aster, plantain and spurreys.

Until recently the estuaries of north-western England have been relatively free from spartina, but now this invader has begun to colonise Morecambe Bay, one of the world's most important areas for wading birds such as dunlin, knot and oystercatchers, and naturalists are rightly concerned.

There has been some confusion regarding the origin of the plant, but it now seems to be generally accepted that our native *Spartina maritima* crossed with the American cord-grass *Spartina townsendii*. Two sorts of

57

hybrids were produced, *Spartina* × *townsendii* which is infertile and *Spartina anglica* which produces fertile seeds. *Spartina anglica* is causing most concern since its seeds can float, making this variety very difficult to eradicate.

Spartina thrives best in mud. It can restrict the flow of water, accelerating the build-up of silt and thus causing problems for river traffic heading for ports and also for seaside resorts anxious to keep their bathing beaches clear. Whenever clumps are allowed to grow to a considerable size before being removed the trapped silt can cause problems, even allowing the build-up of radioactive chemicals, especially in north-western estuaries which have nuclear plants in close proximity.

Spartina must therefore be tackled immediately it is discovered and must be destroyed before this build-up occurs; this is usually achieved by spraying with the herbicide Dalapon. Then comes the real controversy as

Spartina colonising an estuarial mudflat, producing a dense mat of vegetation which accelerates the build-up of silt. *John Clegg*

conservationists line up to complain about the use of poisonous chemicals! In fact Dalapon is less dangerous to other forms of wildlife than many compounds, but the timing of the spraying is crucial; it should be done immediately before a high tide and also if possible during rain so that any excess chemical is quickly diluted.

We can be sure that we have not heard the last of Nature's supergrass, nor of the controversial measures which are essential to remove it. I am aware that many naturalists do not agree that the spraying of toxic chemicals is ever justified, but surely this is better than allowing quantities of radioactive waste to build up in the estuarial mud held in place by spartina.

A study of any estuary must involve firstly a study of the organisms in the water itself and secondly a consideration of the surrounding plants and animals. Where mud predominates a salt marsh is likely to be the climax vegetation, whereas where sand is dominant then the binding action of marram grass will be required with the resultant formation of a sand dune system. It is life in the estuarine water itself, however, which is the main interest of those who study the wildlife of rivers.

Life in estuarine water

The salinity in an estuary will vary according to the height of the tide and the inland rainfall which affects the volume of fresh water reaching the estuary, so animals and plants living in estuaries must be able to cope with extremes in salinity. Despite individual variations estuaries do, however, fall into two basic types. Some estuaries have the same salinity from the top to the bottom because the fresh and seawater mix completely and marine species are able to penetrate into the whole area, while in other estuaries the seawater is driven under the river water and the salt content therefore varies from level to level and the distribution of plants and animals appears to be patchy.

Organisms which live permanently in estuaries have the difficulty of adaptation to overcome, but once established they find few competitors and numbers can build up very quickly. Such creatures can be divided into three groups. Firstly there are marine organisms which have moved into the estuary; then there are freshwater organisms which have travelled downstream; and thirdly there are species which actually evolved in the estuary itself. The marine animals include crustaceans such as crabs, prawns and barnacles, molluscs such as periwinkles, cockles, tellins and mussels, and the round worms (annelids), represented by the lugworm and the ragworm. Both the flounder and the goby are marine fish now well adapted to life in the estuary.

Crabs

Crabs belong to the decapod crustaceans; they have five pairs of limbs, four of which are used for walking plus one very fierce looking pair of pincers. These are best seen by turning the crab on to its back, taking care to avoid being nipped by the pincers. In this position it is possible to determine the sex of the common shore crab (*Carcinus maenas*) by looking at the shape of the flap-like abdomen. The male's abdomen is narrow and divided into five segments, while that of the female is much broader and divided into seven segments. The shore crab can always be recognised by five tooth-shaped structures towards the edge of the shell on either side of the eyes. The colour varies a great deal, some specimens being green, some brown and others even bright orange, and the hardy creature also shows great tolerance to changes of salinity, being quite happy in estuaries where the dilution of salt is as low as six parts per thousand. Shore crabs have adapted to life in estuaries and can even breed there, but they are unable to cope with the low winter temperatures found there and migrate to the open sea during the winter months.

Prawns and shrimps

It is possible to confuse the estuarine prawn (*Palaemonetes varians*) and the edible shrimp (*Crangon crangon*), which is so common in Morecambe Bay. The body of a shrimp is much more compressed than that of a prawn, there is a short projection called a rostrum at the front of the body and only one pair of appendages possesses pincers. In prawns all the limbs have pincers and the rostrum is considerably longer. The genus *Palaemonetes* contains more than twenty species, but only three live in the sea.

The mechanism by which the estuarine prawn combats changes in salinity is fascinating. At sea the prawn maintains the concentration of salt in its blood below that of the seawater, and this means that water is withdrawn from its body by a process known as osmosis. Osmosis is defined as the movement of water from a place of high concentration to one of low concentration, passing through a living membrane, the membrane in this case being the prawn's body. The prawn compensates for this by drinking large quantities of seawater. As it moves into an estuary where the water is between 60 and 70 per cent of the concentration of sea water the strength of salt in the water is equal to the strength of salt in the animal's blood and the prawn need do nothing. This estuarial environment is therefore the region in which it is most common. Further into the river the fresh water dilutes the salt and large quantities of water enter the prawn's body by osmosis, a situation to which the prawn reacts by producing large volumes of urine.

Barnacles

At first glance barnacles seem to have shells and they therefore bear a superficial resemblance to molluscs, especially when seen on exposed surfaces. When they are covered with seawater, however, these beautiful creatures can be seen in their true light. When they are feeding small plates covering the top of the animal open to reveal feathery feeding limbs called cirri which seem to comb the water and filter out small organisms. Although it is found in estuaries the native species, *Balanoides balanoides*, which has six outer plates, is not very tolerant of diluted sea water. *Elminius modestus,* which has only four outer plates and was accidentally introduced into Britain from Australia during the Second World War, is much more tolerant of estuarine conditions.

Periwinkles

Both univalve and bivalve molluscs normally found in the sea have proved well able to penetrate into estuaries, two species in particular occurring some distance up the rivers. These are the edible winkle (*Littorina littorea*), which has a shell up to 2.5 cm (1 inch) across, and the well-named rough winkle (*Littorina saxatilis*), which is only about 1.0 cm (0.4 inch) across but seems able to cope with much more diluted seawater as well as being able to withstand drier and more exposed conditions, and therefore penetrates further up the river.

Despite being closely related, the two have very different breeding strategies. The edible winkle lays its eggs in the sea and the developing larvae are dispersed on the currents and have to fend for themselves, while the rough periwinkle gives birth to live young which it actually broods for a short time.

Cockles

These bivalve molluscs belong to a family specialising in burrowing in sand or mud while feeding and breathing through a pair of siphons, one drawing in a current of water, the other expelling it. The most common species is the edible cockle (*Cerastoderma edule*), which can exist in salinities as low as seventeen parts per thousand. The ribbed surface of the cockle shell probably helps it to grip the sand or mud and prevents it from sinking too far below the surface. In addition to the radiating ridges cockles also have a series of concentric growth lines which can be used to calculate age in much the same way that trees can be aged by reference to their annual rings. During the summer, when food is plentiful, the rate of growth can be as much as one millimetre a week, but in winter growth is very much reduced and the cold weather growth shows up as a narrow ring which can be used to indicate age.

Tellins

Tellins are bivalve molluscs which thrive in estuaries and provide food for many waders including dunlin (*Calidris alpina*), redshank (*Tringa totanus*) and knot (*Calidris canutus*). The commonest species is the thin tellin (*Tellina tenuis*), the shells of which rarely exceed 1.25 cm (0.5 inch) in length and which vary in colour from white through shades of yellow to a delicate pink. It is, however, not too tolerant of dilution and therefore tends to be replaced in estuarine conditions by the Baltic tellin (*Macoma balthica*), which varies in colour from white to crimson and has a thicker and less flattened shell than the thin tellin. It can tolerate both low temperatures and dilution much more easily than other tellins and received its name because of its abundance in the Baltic, where both these conditions are very apparent. I have frequently found it up to a mile up the rivers which drain into Morecambe Bay, where *Macoma balthica* is the most common mollusc.

Mussels

Blue edible mussels (*Mytilus edulis*) need a solid support in order to attach themselves by means of sticky structures called byssus threads; they are, for example, found on the piers of bridges spanning the tidal reaches of rivers. Providing the salinity is greater than five parts per thousand, mussels thrive.

As implied by its name, the blue edible mussel is food for humans as well as seabirds, the most productive commercial beds being around the mouths of estuaries, especially Morecambe Bay, the Wash and Conway Bay. Like cockles, mussels have a pair of siphons which enable them to filter the water efficiently, but in polluted areas poisons can quickly be accumulated and many traditional mussel beds have been destroyed by new sewage or industrial outfalls. All mussels intended for the table should be kept a couple of days in clean water to ensure the removal of debris, and collection from polluted areas should be avoided.

Worms

Two species of annelid are found in brackish water. The lugworm (*Arenicola marina*), a sedentary animal commonly over 10 cm (4 inches) in length, lives in a U-shaped burrow and feeds by swallowing sand at the head end and expelling the waste at the tail end. Lugworm burrows can be identified by the depression caused by suction at one end and the worm cast at the other. Lugworm is a favourite food of many estuarine fish and is much sought after as bait by anglers.

The ragworm (*Nereis diversicolor*), which can also reach 10 cm (4 inches), is likewise a juicy morsel for fish but is a much more active animal, often penetrating higher up the river; it can tolerate a salinity as low as one part per thousand, although it is unable to breed in such conditions.

Flounder

Flounders (*Platichthys flesus*) can reach a length of almost 50 cm (20 inches), which makes them much prized by fishermen. They will venture much further into rivers than any other flat fish. The flounder is pale on the undersurface but its mottled brown back lacks the bright orange spots typical of plaice (*Pleuronectes platessa*).

Goby

The goby (*Pomatoschistus microps*), one of the most abundant of all estuary fish, can penetrate deep into the river but it must always return to the sea to breed. In freshwater it feeds upon chironomid larvae and can even be a rival to the minnow, while in the estuary its main diet is shrimps. Gobies can be recognised by the presence of two dorsal fins, while the pelvic fins on the underside of the body are fused together to form a sucker which can be used to attach the fish to stones; it can thus resist removal by tide or river current.

While the goby is well adapted to life in the estuary it has obviously not evolved there, since it must return to salt water to breed. Few organisms seem to have been able to evolve in the estuary itself, but there are three fascinating creatures which have managed to solve the problems of estuarine breeding, *Hydrobia*, *Cerophium* and *Gammarus daubeni*.

Hydrobia

This tiny snail, measuring only 0.6 cm (0.25 inch), was described in the eighteenth century by the much travelled and skilful naturalist Thomas Pennent as 'the size of a grain of wheat'. If wheat feeds man, then *Hydrobia* surely feeds the birds, especially the shelduck (*Tadorna tadorna*) which sweeps up thousands with its bill from the estuarine mud flats, particularly on an ebbing tide.

There are three species of *Hydrobia*, but they cannot be separated unless dissected and examined under a microscope. They all have an intriguing daily cycle of behaviour geared to the tides, and although they can penetrate up the river they cannot go beyond the tidal reach. As the tide ebbs *Hydrobia* crawl over the mud feeding upon the detritus and tiny diatoms left exposed. When they have eaten they burrow down into the mud to await the next tide. As the water begins to cover the mud the snails emerge and each tiny snail spins a mucous raft which floats and allows *Hydrobia* to filter out its food. Gradually the raft disintegrates, and as the tide ebbs the snail settles down on the mud and the cycle is repeated.

Cerophium volutator

This little crustacean seldom exceeds one centimetre (0.4 inch) in length, but what it lacks in size it more than makes up for in numbers, which is perhaps just as well because it is an important item in the diet of many fish and birds, including waders such as the sanderling (*Calidris alba*).

Cerophium is able to survive in salinities of less than three parts per thousand, but it needs this level to increase to five parts per thousand before it can moult and to eight before the breeding cycle can be satisfactorily accomplished.

Gammarus daubeni

This marine creature has evolved from a freshwater ancestor and like the last species described it can withstand very low concentrations of salt. The limiting factor for *G. daubeni* appears to be its inability to withstand competition with *Gammarus pulex*, which has a far higher reproductive rate. What is interesting is that *Gammarus pulex* does not occur in Ireland, where *Gammarus daubeni* occurs both in the estuaries and in fresh water. There is a great deal yet to be discovered about its life history. Why, for example, are only males produced in water with a temperature below 5°C, only females in a temperature above 6°C, and a mixture of both sexes between these two levels?

Freshwater organisms at home in estuaries

Tubifex is an aquatic worm so tough that it can not only resist very high levels of pollution but also seems able to cope easily with increased salinity. The water louse *Asellus* appears to be able to live in an estuary, but once the salinity increases beyond five parts per thousand its reproduction is prevented and thus it can never be a permanent part of the fauna of an estuary.

Generally speaking insects are unable to cope with salinity, although the larva of the caddisfly *Limniphilus affinus* has proved able to develop into an adult providing the salinity does not rise above seventeen parts per thousand. Such conditions are sometimes common in the pools of salt marshes, especially in summers in which there is higher than average rainfall, the classic example being that of 1985.

Opposite: The estuary of the River Kent, one of the rivers draining into Morecambe Bay, which remains a haven for all kinds of wild life including birds.   *John Clegg*

The insectivorous sundew (*Drosera rotundi-folia*).   *Ron Freethy*

Red rattle (*Pedicularis palustris*), otherwise known as lousewort.   *Ron Freethy*

Marsh marigold (*Caltha palustris*) growing near the edge of a river.   *Ron Freethy*

CHAPTER FIVE

Plants of the River

ATTEMPTS to classify rivers into zones according to the plants found along their length are not nearly so successful as those using fish as indicators. There are, however, plants which are typically found in areas where rivers rise and as the waters slow other plants grow which are less disturbed by the current and whose roots have a more stable bed in which to anchor.

Upland plants

The rain and snow that falls high on the soggy uplands seeps through the saturated ground, eventually to spawn the streams that combine and unite to form the rivers. The leaching effect of this percolating rain and melt water often renders upland soil deficient in vital elements, particularly nitrates, which plants need to produce proteins.

Some plants such as upland grasses are able to survive on low chemical levels, but the catchment areas of many rivers are dotted with plants which make use of special strategies to overcome such deficiencies. Eyebright and yellow rattle, for example, live as partial parasites, and lousewort also thrives as a partial parasite in these areas. Other plants found near the sources of upland rivers are butterwort and sundew, both of which increase their intake of nitrates by trapping and devouring insects. The recent controversy surrounding acid rain (see chapter eleven) sometimes appears to suggest that no plants can grow in acid conditions, but cotton grass, rushes and bog asphodel seem to be able to grow in conditions which are surprisingly acid.

Eyebright (*Euphrasia officinalis* agg)

Now separated into many sub-species, the tiny eyebrights seldom grow taller than 5 cm (2 inches) but the white, purple-streaked flowers have yellow anthers which shine out from the green grasses among which they live. Their name eyebright indicates an ancient use for the plant, which was in the production of soothing eye washes. The roots of eyebright are found to be wound around those of grasses, and on close examination it is seen that tiny suckers actually penetrate the tissues of the grass. Some food is obtained by this method, leading to eyebright being defined as a partial or semi-parasite.

Yellow rattle *(Rhinanthus minor)*

This species is not restricted to upland areas but occurs on grassland at all altitudes, including exposed areas of sand dunes. The yellow flowers nod in the breezes from June until late August, after which the seed head is blown and the seeds within rattle together as the plant is shaken by the wind, this being responsible for its vernacular name.

Red rattle *(Pedicularis palustris)*

Lousewort, otherwise known as red rattle, is much more common than yellow rattle in upland regions, and in some areas sphagnum moss and red rattle can be the dominant plants. At one time when the moorlands of Britain were often the scene of battles sphagnum moss was gathered and stuffed into wounds; not only does the moss soak up blood just as well as it soaks up water but sphagnum also contains a chemical which arrests bleeding (an astringent). As recently as the First World War this absorbent moss was part of a soldier's field kit.

A sundew photographed on Borth Bog, not far from Aberystwyth. The sticky leaves trap flies which are digested by the plant, providing it with elements which it cannot get from the soil in the wet barren uplands on which it grows.　　　　*Alan W. Heath*

Red rattle is a member of the snapdragon family, as is yellow rattle, the vernacular name again deriving from the seeds rattling about inside the capsule. The name lousewort has two possible derivations. Some suggest that the plant's scent attracts lice; a more sensible suggestion would seem to be that it grows in damp, unhealthy areas where sheep tend to be prone to attack by parasites, and the presence of the plant is commonly if erroneously blamed for this.

Butterwort *(Pinguicula vulgaris)*

Rising from a rosette of sticky leaves, the flowers of butterwort are carried on long stems 15 cm (6 inches) into the air, where they are easily pollinated by insects. Any insect unwise enough to land upon the leaves instead of upon a flower is immediately trapped; it triggers off a mechanism which causes the leaves to fold over and create what amounts to a temporary stomach, digestive juices then being created to break down the tissues of the prey. The resultant 'soup' is absorbed into the body of the plant, enabling butterwort to thrive even on bare rock; they are one of the first plants to be noticed near the source of many rivers. The word *Pinguicula* means fat, which is an accurate description of the leaves. If these are chopped up and added to milk the chemicals contained in the leaves coagulate the milk; for this reason the leaves were used in the manufacture of butter.

Sundew *(Drosera rotundifolia)*

Frequently found in boggy areas, the common sundew has spoon-shaped leaves covered in tiny hairs, each with a globule of a glue-like substance at its tip. In some drier areas a rarer species, the long-leaved sundew *(Drosera intermedia)* occurs; and the even rarer great sundew *(Drosera anglica)*, with its long, tapering leaves, may be found in such places. The sticky, glistening leaves, from which the plant gets its name, trap flies which are digested to provide elements which are rare in wet barren uplands. The flowers are borne on long stalks, which prevent pollinating flies from being trapped and eaten.

Cotton grass *(Eriophorum angustifolium)*

Cotton grass is wrongly named; it is not a grass but a sedge. Sedges can be distinguished by their triangular stems. There are actually four species of cotton grass, namely broad leaved *(E. latifolium)*, slender *(E. gracile)* and harestail cotton grass *(E. vaginatum)* but the common *(E. angustifolium)* is the dominant species.

During early spring the flowering heads are yellow, with pollen hanging from the anthers. In May and June the cottony seed heads bobbing in the breeze help to make a moorland walk both pleasant and safe—pleasant because of the pleasing sight of the wispy white heads, and safe because the plant grows on the wettest and therefore most dangerous places and provides adequate warning to the walker. Overhead the curlew bubbles his breeding song, the snipe drums and the trilling skylark soars high. Beneath the feet lie thick layers of peat, formed from dead cotton grass being pressed into an oozing ground

Harestail cotton grass grow-ing on Grindon Moor, Derby-shire.   *Alan W. Heath*

which contains insufficient oxygen to allow the dead stems to decay. Many northern rivers rise on cotton grass moors where the white heads contrast with the smaller delicate white flowers of heath bedstraw (*Galium palustre*), the blue of common speedwell (*Veronica officinalis*), and the delicate yellows of tormentil (*Potentilla erecta*).

Bog asphodel *(Narthecium ossifragum)*

Ossifragum is a Latin name meaning bone-breaking; it was once believed that animals which ate the bog asphodel plant developed brittle bones. I think a more likely explanation is that bog asphodel grows on land full of mires and pitfalls, and even sure-footed animals fall all too easily under such conditions. The plant seldom grows higher than 15 cm (6 inches) but its lovely yellow star-like flowers, which darken to deep orange as they ripen, light up many a dull moorland. Its colour shines out from masses of bracken (*Pteridium aquilinum*), cross leaved heath (*Erica tetralix*), cowberry (*Vaccinium vitis-idaea*) and bilberry (*Vaccinium myrtillus*). Wood sage (*Teucrium scorodonia*) is, despite its name, common on these high moors, often growing close to the highly perfumed bog myrtle (*Myrica gale*).

70

Few if any plants can survive in the turbulent infant river itself, but as soon as the current becomes calmer the first water plants put in an appearance.

Plants of the middle and lower reaches

Stretches of fresh water, even those moving quite quickly, will have five basic areas of plant life, namely microscopic algae; simple plants including the larger algae, liverworts, mosses and ferns; floating flowering plants; fringing plants which are partly submerged, and finally waterside plants which thrive in damp conditions. Although this is not a scientific division, it works very well for the amateur naturalist. In ponds and lakes these regions are quite obvious, but rivers and streams, especially when in spate, can disrupt the zones and flush the plants from their usual niche. In a summer with only average rainfall most plants in the middle and lower reaches grow well and each of the above groups is fully represented.

Microscopic algae

By definition a magnifying glass or, better still, a microscope is needed to see these plants; because they play such an important role in freshwater food chains, some mention must be made of them. It should be stressed that there are few more beautiful sights in nature than these organisms when seen even under the low power of the cheapest microscope.

Mention of plankton brings to mind thoughts of the arctic seas and of the huge whales which filter it from the sea, but plankton also occurs in fresh water, including ditches, streams and rivers, and can be extracted using a sieve made from the cheapest of materials. Take an old pair of tights or a nylon stocking, remove one leg and then make a hole in the foot; push a small jar through this hole and secure it firmly with string or wire. If this contraption is trawled through the water a collection of small organisms including microscopic algae will collect in the jar. To identify these you will need a key to freshwater algae (see bibliography), which are classified according to the pigments they contain; there are the green algae (Chlorophyceae), yellow-green algae (Xanthophyceae), golden brown (Chrysophyceae), the diatoms (Bacillariophyceae), olive green flagellates (Cryptophyceae), armoured flagellates (Dinophyceae), green flagellates (Euglenophyceae), red algae (Rhodophyceae) and the blue-green algae (Myxophyceae). It is obviously beyond the scope of this book to deal effectively with this group, but a brief description of a fascinating group of species may serve to whet the appetite.

Chlamydomonas, Eudorina, Pandorina *and* Volvox

Although more common in still water, *Chlamydomonas*, one of the most important of the green algae, is found in slow-moving rivers. There are many species grouped in the genus *Chlamydomonas*; all can be recognised by their oval body cell (there is only one), propelled by a pair of flagella of the same length, and by the presence of a single red 'eye spot' which is sensitive to light. Within the single cell of *Chlamydomonas* all body functions, including photosynthesis and reproduction, have to go on much as they do in more complicated organisms. A multicellular body obviously allows a greater degree of specialisation within the organism. Colonial green algae based upon 'Chlamydomonas-like' individuals may well show the early development of this specialisation, and a possible sequence is demonstrated by *Eudorina, Pandorina* and *Volvox*. These three consist of an increasing number of cells; in the case of *Volvox* hundreds of individuals are embedded in a mass of mucilage. Not all the cells are capable of reproduction, thus providing an example of early division of labour in the plant kingdom. *Volvox* is found in most areas of fresh water, even slow-moving rivers, and is large enough to be seen by the naked eye. It is when it is viewed under the microscope, even one of low power, that *Volvox* is seen to be one of nature's most beautiful creatures.

Opposite: *Volvox* seen through the microscope. The animal on the left is a nauplius larva of a crustacean, *Diaptomus.*
John Clegg

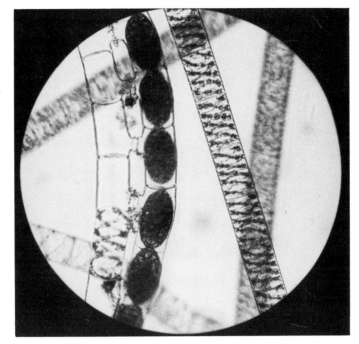

Right: *Spirogyra—* normal and conjugating. This is possibly the best-known of the larger algae.   *Alan W. Heath*

Simple plants

Although normally known as the simple plants, a better description of this group might be the non-flowering plants, because many of them are anything but simple. Life began in the sea and from there moved into fresh water, finally emerging on to dry land at quite a late stage in the evolutionary process. The middle stages of this sequence can be seen by reference to the larger algae, liverworts, mosses, ferns, and finally the horsetails.

Larger algae

Spirogyra is perhaps the best known of the larger algae to students of biology since it is the type described in all biology examination texts. This filamentous ladder-like form is found mainly in still waters; it is common in pools left when rivers and streams overflow their banks and also in sheltered spots under banks. The filaments are not branched and have a green spiral-shaped chloroplast running through each. This is the site of food manufacture. *Spirogyra* is easily fragmented, and since each part is able to grow into a new filament the species becomes common during the summer and is eaten by many small animals; it is thus an important starting point for aquatic food chains.

Perhaps stimulated by a fall in autumn temperatures, two filaments drift together, swellings arising along the length of each. These swellings first touch and then their walls break down, the contents of one (the male) fusing with the other (the female). The 'fertilised egg' forms a protective wall around itself and sinks to the bottom when the parent filaments die. Germination occurs in response to the increased temperatures of spring.

Spirogyra is not the only filamentous alga found in and around rivers, another being *Ulothrix*, which has its chloroplast arranged as a band rather than a spiral; its filaments are also unbranched. *Cladophora* is common in running water and is often found attached to sticks and stones, being recognised by its rough branched filaments. These may often be found rolled up together in bundles as large as a tennis ball. Belcher and Swale's guide (see bibliography) is an easy-to-use key which enables the newcomer to get to know the common species quickly.

Stoneworts

The stoneworts are a fascinating and well-named group of simple plants found in slow-moving rivers and also in ponds, but only in those

A stonewort, *Nitella*, one of a group of simple plants found in slow-moving rivers containing hard water. *John Clegg*

containing hard water. The green brittle plants, which can grow up to a foot (30.5 cm) high, extract calcium salts from the water of rivers flowing over limestone, the rivers Wharfe and Ribble being particularly good for stoneworts. Some of the chalk streams of lowland Britain are also suitable areas for finding these plants. The stems of the stoneworts are jointed and branched, while in some the branchlets are forked as in the genus *Nitella*. Species belonging to the *Chara* genus have unforked branchlets.

Liverworts and mosses

The Bryophytes are plants which require wet conditions in order to reproduce efficiently. They are divided into the liverworts (Hepaticae) and mosses (Musci). The student of fresh waters is likely to come across several species of both liverworts and mosses.

Liverworts are usually recognised by having a flattened body called a thallus, from the underside of which arise rhizoids made up of only one cell. These structures serve to anchor the plant, but are not equivalent to the roots of higher plants since they play no part in the absorption of water. Plants associated so intimately with water find it easy to absorb water all over the surface of the thallus.

Often found floating just below the surface of still pools in streams and rivers is the floating crystalwort (*Riccia fluitans*), which has a thin, forked, ribbon-like thallus about 5 cm (2 inches) long and has no rhizoids. This species reproduces vegetatively, but when the plants are stranded after a flood they are stimulated to produce sexual organs and the life cycle is completed. Another species commonly found around streams is the great scented liverwort (*Conocephalum conicum*), which is very dark green and when crushed produces a very attractive scent. *Pellia epiphylla*, with its light green thallus and dark circular spore capsules, is also common, as is *Marchantia polymorpha* with its darker spotted thallus and capsules looking like tiny toadstools with crinkled edges.

Mosses are separated from liverworts by their leafy stems and also by their rhizoids, which are made up of many cells. Mosses are found in upland areas, even those which are extremely acid. The bog mosses (*Sphagnum* sp) are particularly common, but also found is the bright green long-beaked water moss (*Eurhynchium riparoides*). The leaves of this species have serrated edges and the reproductive capsules have beaked lids. The yellow-brown branches of feather moss (*Drepanocladus fluitans*) are often found immersed in waters of upland streams and pools.

As the river widens and deepens the willow moss (*Fontinalis antipyretica*) thrives, its long hair-like threads billowing out in the current like a girl's hair in the wind. Close to the bank, often splashed by the current, grows the long-beaked thread moss (*Minium longirostrum*), easily recognised by its large pointed leaves near the tips of the stem, and also by the yellow beak-like structure on the capsule.

Ferns

In Britain we have no native ferns which are purely aquatic but the fairy 'moss' (*Azolla filiculoides*), introduced from America for use in aquaria, has now established itself in the wild. It is man's interference with rivers which has provided ferns with a chance to become riverside plants. Hanging in festoons from bridges and retaining walls is the common polypody (*Polypodium vulgare*) and wall rue (*Asplenium ruta-muraria*), while growing in cracks in the masonry are lush fronds of hart's tongue fern (*Phyllitus scolopendrium*) and the delicate branches of maidenhair spleenwort (*Asplenium trichomanes*).

Floating flowering plants

In the calmer areas of streams and rivers are to be found some freely floating plants such as duckweed, frogbit, Canadian pondweed, water lily and the attractive water crowfoots.

Duckweeds (Lemna)

Tiny pieces of flattened stems with roots trailing beneath them; that is the typical structure of the duckweeds, which although more common in still water can often cover the slower reaches of rivers with a carpet of green. The tiny insect-pollinated flowers push out above the water level, but in truth the flowers are seldom seen.

The exact key which turns on a plant's flowering period has long been a puzzle to scientists, but it is now known that a derivative of salicylic acid is involved. This chemical, better known to us as aspirin, is present in plants, no doubt in connection with flowering. As we shall see, aspirin has been extracted commercially both from meadowsweet and from the bark of willow trees. If you have duckweed in your garden pond which is not producing flowers you may well be able to persuade it to do so by adding aspirin to the water!

Frogbit (Hydrocharis morsus-ranae)

Frogbit is not a common river plant but grows well in drainage ditches. It tends to float on the surface during the summer months, the initial growth being from a rosette of leaves, beneath which hangs a beard-like tangle of roots.

Like duckweed, the white three-petalled flowers seldom produce fertile seeds—perhaps they also need an aspirin—and vegetative propagation seems the rule. In response to the cooler temperatures of

76

autumn, frogbit produces winter buds which contain immature plants surrounded by heavy deposits of food. When the parent plant dies these buds sink, the embryo using up the food during the colder months. The resulting reduction in weight causes the frogbit to float to the surface, by which time it is summer again and life can continue.

Frogbit is also related to Canadian pondweed (*Elodea canadensis*) and the water soldier (*Stratiotes aloides*), which are also found in slow-moving rivers and canals.

Water lilies

Two species of water lily occur in flowing water, the white water lily (*Nymphaea alba*), which is found throughout Britain, and the less widely distributed but much more numerous yellow water lily (*Nuphar lutea*). This latter species has huge leaves with a central stalk which gives great stability and prevents it overturning. These stalks can be very long,

Seen from a distance duckweed can look like a solid carpet of green, but close up it has a different look. This is lesser duckweed, with a few plants of greater duckweed on the right. *John Clegg*

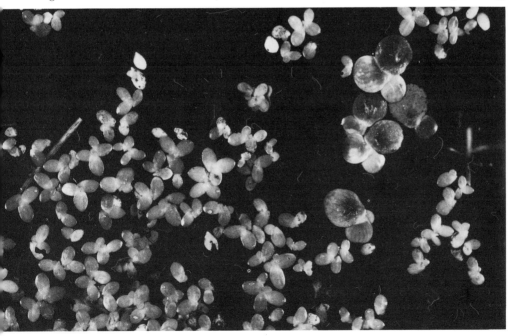

allowing yellow water lilies to grow from roots at depths of around 3 metres (10 feet). It seems that the faster the average river flow, the smaller are the leaves, thus cutting down resistance to the water.

The white water lily has larger and more attractive flowers than the yellow, and during rough weather the flower closes up tightly and sinks beneath the surface. The fruit is a large berry which actually ripens under water. Each seed, called an aril, is surrounded by a spongy tissue, enabling it to float to the surface and be thus carried away from the parent plant. Gradually the air bubbles trapped in the spongy tissue disperse and the seed sinks to the bottom, where it germinates.

The smaller, less attractive flowers of the yellow species smell like brandy, thus earning their vernacular name of 'brandy bottles'; the seed vessels are also bottle shaped. The fruit is not provided with spongy tissue and develops above the water, but it does have an oily coat which holds some air and thus allows efficient dispersal. As the fruit wall decays, the air is released and the embryo sinks to the bottom.

Thus both species of water lily show ingenious adaptations to their aquatic habitat, a feature also typical of the water crowfoots.

Water crowfoot (Ranunculus aquatilis)

Many species of this delicate member of the buttercup family are found in rivers and streams, including celery leaved crowfoot (*R. sceleratus*), ivy leaved crowfoot (*R. hederaceus*) and *Ranunculus fluitans*, which is a tough species often having submerged stems over 6 metres (20 feet) in length and able to root in the fastest-moving of our rivers. Indeed, *R. fluitans* may often slow the current to such an extent that the river may start to silt up, allowing fringing plants to gain a roothold.

Members of the water crowfoot group have three distinct types of leaf. Some leaves which are kidney shaped and float on the surface, held in position by stout stems, would not survive in the swirling undercurrents of the faster rivers; plants growing in such conditions have longer, narrower and finely divided leaves which are thus ideally shaped for resisting currents. There are also some leaves which are intermediate between these extremes.

Fringing plants

There can be few more pleasant occupations for a naturalist than splashing around in the shallow swamp water near a river bank or among the tangled vegetation of an ox-bow formed from an isolated meander. Prominent here are monkey flower, watercress, yellow iris, bulrush, amphibious bistort, water dropwort, bog bean, mare's tail, brooklime and the spearworts.

Above: Water crowfoot growing in the River Ribble in Lancashire. Other fringing plants are gaining a roothold on the right. *Michael Edwards*

Right: A close-up of the flowers of water crowfoot. *Alan W. Heath*

Monkey flower (Mimulus guttatus)

This attractive perennial with its large yellow flowers, spotted and blotched with scarlet, lights up many a dull industrial river and shows a quite remarkable resistance to pollution. It is now so common that it is difficult to believe that it was introduced from North America and has only been found in the wild in Britain since 1830.

Introduced about the same time was Himalayan balsam, also called policeman's helmet (*Impatiens glandulifera*), another species which has proved very resistant to pollution and often dominates the banks of industrialised rivers. The purplish pink flowers can stand up to 2 metres (6.5 feet) high and are pollinated by bumblebees. If the normal pollinators fail to do their job, some flowers close tightly, pressing the reproductive parts together and fertilising themselves, a phenomenon which is called cleistogamy. The seed cases are tightly twisted and 'explode' at the slightest touch, hurling the seeds several metres from the parents. The seeds are light enough to float, which may well account for the plant's rapid spread throughout the waterways of Britain.

Watercress (Nasturtium officinale)

One of the few aquatic plants to have real commercial value, the watercress is a hairless perennial with green leaves rich in vitamin C. The white flowers, which appear from May to October, are typical of the Cruciferae family, the four petals being arranged in the form of a cross. Watercress thrives in shallow flowing water, especially if the bed of the river is composed of limestone. The young succulent plants have long been popular in salads and were once extensively used as an aphrodisiac.

Care must be taken to distinguish watercress, a crucifer, from the umbellifer fool's watercress (*Apium nodiflorum*). The latter is poisonous, but it can be distinguished by its pointed leaflets, which are finely toothed; watercress leaves have no teeth and are more rounded.

Yellow iris (Iris pseudacorus)

One of the most attractive of riverside plants, the yellow iris has

Yellow flag   *Carole Pugh*

delightful yellow flowers and sharp-edged leaves which have inflicted many a deep cut on those who carelessly gather them. The leaves can be over a metre long (39.4 inches) and 2.5 cm (1 inch) wide. The flower is thought by some to be the original fleur-de-lys of French heraldry, but other authorities think the true lily was the more obvious influence; it seems to the present writer that *Iris pseudacorus* has the better claim. The sheer beauty of its flower inspired the poet John Clare to write in his 'Recollections after a Ramble':

> Some, with many an anxious pain,
> Childish wishes to pursue
> From the poundhead gazed in vain
> On the flag-flowers' yellow hue.

The thick subterranean stem, called a rhizome, thrives beneath the water and puts up growths each year, the yellow flowers, often 7.5 cm (3 inches) across, being pollinated by bees.

Bulrush (Scirpus lacustris)

At one time this species was called the pool rush, which describes its habitat perfectly. The only thing which is wrong with that name is that the plant is not a rush at all, but related to cotton grass and the sedges. When the species grows in still water the leaves tend to be short and flat, but when exposed to the current of a river they become strap-like and a great deal longer. The stem, which can grow to heights of over 2 m (6.5 feet), is erect and spongy, rising from a thick, often potato-like, subterranean stem. The hermaphroditic flowers are grouped in spikelets. Although still cultivated for decorative purposes, the bulrush has gone out of fashion for chair seats and tough mats.

Amphibious bistort (Polygonum amphibium)

Sometimes called the sweaty-sock plant because of its smell, this attractive-looking plant often dominates the fringes of slow-moving rivers. Its pinkish-red flowers can grow to heights of 75 cm (29.5 inches). As its name implies, the species is amphibious, those plants growing in water differing markedly from the land-based individuals. In the aquatic form roots may arise from the nodes, the stems and leaves float, and both are glabrous (hairless); the stems of the land-based form are very erect and only put out roots from the lower nodes, while the plant may also be slightly hairy.

Water dropwort

There are several species of water dropwort and care is neeeded to separate them, but T.G. Tutin's book is a great help (see bibliography).

The parsley water dropwort (*Oenanthe lachenalii*) is a widespread species often found in fens, but also common is the hemlock water dropwort (*Oenanthe crocata*), which flowers from May to July in areas where small streams feed into rivers or marshes. The river water dropwort (*Oenanthe fluviatilis*) has submerged leaves and occurs in the slow-moving waters of south-eastern England.

Bogbean (Menyanthes trifoliata)

This species has also been called the buckbean, and although not common is widely distributed. The specific name indicates that the leaves are divided into three lobes, these being lance shaped with prominently toothed outer edges. Bogbean arises from a rhizome, a form of growth favoured by a large number of perennial emergent plants. The name I remember for this plant during my youth spent in the Lake District was beck-bean; beck was the old Norse word for a stream. It belongs to the gentian family and has their typical bitter taste, which led to its use both in brewing and medicine; the dried leaves were often infused with hot water and drunk as a tonic tea. The hairy pink and white flowers bloom from April to July and are carried high above the surface of the water, often producing a spectacular blaze of colour in a meadow.

Marestail (Hippuris vulgaris)

Marestail is a strange-looking plant with leaves rich in silicon, once used as pan-scrubbers or as a scouring powder. The plant bears a superficial resemblance to the horse-tails, which are of course flowerless. The flowers of marestail are quite small and difficult to find, since they are very much reduced; there are no petals at all and even the sepals are represented only by a rim around the ovary. Such a flower, with only one stamen and one carpel, could hardly be reduced much more and must therefore be wind pollinated, since insects are hardly likely to notice it; and in any event the plant does not produce nectar.

Brooklime (Veronica beccabunga)

Looking rather like germander speedwell (*Veronica chamaedrys*), but distinguished by its hairless stems, brooklime is typical of plants which grow in water. From May to September the lovely blue flowers arise from succulent procumbent stems which straddle ditches and streams. Brooklime often shares its habitat with other members of the speedwell family, including the marsh speedwell (*Veronica scutellata*), which grows well in acid conditions, and the widely distributed water speedwell (*Veronica anagallis-aquatica*). Here, too, are found the spearworts, which belong to the Ranunculaceae, the buttercup family.

Lesser spearwort (Ranunculus flammula)

This widespread and at times abundant species grows at the edge of rivers; when the water is shallow and slow moving it may even grow in the middle, the spear-like leaves offering little resistance to the water. The delicate yellow flowers are pollinated by small bees and flies. Lesser spearwort, in addition to being found fringing rivers, is often found along with water forgetmenot (*Myosotis scorpioides*) and marsh cinquefoil (*Potentilla palustris*) in the waterside zone dominated by trees such as alder and willow.

Waterside plants

Those of us who enjoy a quiet stroll by a riverside will soon come across the willows and the alder which overhang the water. In summer their leaves provide cool shade in which fish and other aquatic life can lie up. The submerged roots provide hideaways for all sorts of creatures, including water voles and even otters and mink. The trunks of riverside trees provide resting places for many insects which lay their eggs in the water, while the leaves provide a source of food.

Willows

Willows make up a large genus consisting of species which hybridise and are therefore often difficult to identify. Frequently found by watersides are the pussy willow (*Salix caprea*), weeping willow (*Salix babylonica*), crack willow (*Salix fragilis*) and white willow (*Salix alba*), which is still economically important since it is the species used in the production of cricket bats.

The flowers are in the form of catkins and almost always the sexes are found on separate trees. The flowers of both sexes have nectaries, a sure sign that they are insect pollinated, usually by bees. Many beekeepers deliberately plant willows near their hives because they flower early in the year, ensuring that there is a supply of food for insects emerging from their winter torpor. The flower is carried in the axil of small bracts, the male catkins dying off after shedding their pollen. The female catkins, naturally enough, last longer and eventually develop into a fruit called a capsule; the seed is released from this when it splits. Each seed is carried away by the wind, its journey speeded by a ring of feathery down.

Not all willows grow large enough to be called trees but all were formerly essential items of commerce. The common osier (*Salix viminalis*), for example, never grows tall but often dominates marshland close to rivers. It responds well to pollarding and also grows from suckers. It was harvested in the past and its long flexible branches used in basket work.

I remember one of my earliest lessons in natural history—nay, conservation—coming from an old fenman who told me why he farmed his osiers rather than taking them all. Their roots bind the river banks and prevent erosion and consequent flooding. He pointed out the insects which fed upon the leaves, the bees which pollinated the catkins and the birds which nested in the tangled branches.

Alder (Alnus glutinosa)

The same fenman also showed me an otter's holt under the gnarled roots of a riverside alder. I watched as he cut down a selected few of the trees and cut the timber into blocks which were used to make clogs,

A clogmaker at work—the soles of clogs are made from alder wood, which does not warp when exposed to the wet.
Bill Wilkinson

longer pieces of the timber being sold to make gate posts. A plant 'growing with its feet in water', he told me, would be unlikely to warp when exposed to damp conditions.

I remember also looking at the roots of alders dangling in the water, some looking as pink as raw meat. Many were covered with little bumps called nodules; when cut open and examined under a high-powered microscope these are found to be full of bacteria capable of manufacturing nitrates directly from atmospheric nitrogen, which explains why alder can live in waterlogged soil which has had all essential nutrients leached out of it. As these alder roots decay and also when its leaves fall on to the ground the soil is enriched, often enabling other plants to grow around it.

The waterside flowers are so numerous that to list them all would be impossible in a book of this kind. Mention, however, must be made of the following species: gipsywort, meadowsweet, cuckoo flower, hemp agrimony, butterbur, kingcup, willowherb, ragged robin and marsh woundwort.

Gipsywort (Lycopus europaeus)

Both gipsywort and purple loosestrife (*Lythrum salicaria*) have evolved a fascinating strategy to enable them to cope with occasional periods when the soil in which they live becomes waterlogged and therefore deficient in oxygen. Their roots and stems develop spongy swellings within which are cells acting like miniature oxygen tanks which are topped up with air when conditions become easier.

Gipsywort is related to water mint (*Mentha aquatica*) but is less common in northern Britain than the latter. Gipsywort is easily recognised by its whorls of white flowers which arise near the point where the jagged leaves join the stem. The plant can reach almost 50 cm (19.7 inches) and its stem is square in section. The plant has a long flowering season, a few precocious blooms being found as early as June; a few flowers are still there to brighten the dull days of November. Its generic name *Lycopus* has a Greek root meaning wolf's foot, which is said to derive from the shape of the leaf. This shows a high degree of poetic licence, as does, I think, its vernacular name. Gipsies were supposed to have obtained a dark stain from the plant with which they coloured their skin. My grandmother maintained that gipsywort dye disguised grey hair, an opinion supported by the fact that she had jet black hair until well into her nineties!

Meadowsweet (Filipendula ulmaria)

As already mentioned, both willow and meadowsweet contain substantial quantities of salicylic acid and therefore their use as cures for headaches and as fever-cures was more than likely to be successful.

The tall erect stems of meadowsweet often reach a height of over 1 metre (3.28 feet) and the branches, more numerous towards the tip, bear flowers in large terminal clusters. The scent has a faint trace of almonds and while attractive to most people can usually be guaranteed to deter insects. Its old name was mead-wort; it was used to add flavour to the fermented drink known as mead. Some authorities still prefer the name mead-sweet.

There is little doubt that its presence adds both beauty and perfume to a water meadow or damp riverside, as befits a member of the rose family. It was collected to spread on the floor of churches and houses when these were made of packed earth; it was said that Queen Elizabeth I liked meadowsweet placed in her bed to keep it sweet.

Cuckooflower, lady's smock (Cardamine pratensis)

This pretty plant, with its four petals arranged in the form of a cross, is a member of the Cruciferae family. Its vernacular names of meadow cress and bitter cress indicate its taste and its use in salads as a source of vitamin C. Although our ancestors did not know of vitamins they did know that eating the cress family prevented an unpleasant death from scurvy. Bog pink was yet another country name indicative of its favoured habitat. The nickname lady's smock was given to the plant because the flowers looked like clothes laid out to dry. This confusing list of old names should make us quite glad of scientific names, which do not vary. *Cardamine pratensis* is easy to see in the dusk and is often pollinated by moths which visit it in search of the copious nectar. During the day this ready supply is tapped by day-flying moths, butterflies and many species of beetle.

Hemp agrimony (Eupatorium cannabinum)

Although superficially resembling the carrot family (Umbelliferae), hemp agrimony with its tubular flowers is a member of the daisy (Compositae) family. These primitive flowers are thought to represent an early stage in the development of the family. Each flower appears at first sight to be single but closer examination reveals five separate blooms, the overall effect being a mass of mauve waving in the breeze. The plant is another riverside species producing copious amounts of pollen, which seems to be particularly attractive to butterflies. These are often found in huge numbers among the flowers during July and August. Light, downy seeds are spread by the equinoctial winds of September and October.

Butterbur (Petasites hybridus)

This plant, whose huge leaves often dominate river banks, is also a member of the Compositae family. It has a special place in my affections because it is among the first signs of spring along my local river banks, the flowers always appearing before the leaves just as in the case of the smaller but closely related coltsfoot (*Tussilago farfara*). Both the flowers, which used to be called boghorns, and the leaves arise from a food-rich subterranean rhizome. The boghorns can be up to 30 cm (11.8 inches) in height.

Butterbur is an example of a dioecious plant with male and female flowers carried on separate plants; the looser, shorter clusters of small flowers are the males, while the females, carried on larger heads, are much longer and on longer spikes. Only the male flowers possess nectar, so it is hard to see why large insects should wish to visit the female plant, and it is therefore thought that butterbur is pollinated by small flies attracted by the faint smell of rotting flesh exuded from the flower. Another possibility is that the large female flowers are used as shelters by bees during the cold wet days of early spring, and the visitors could carry pollen with them.

An old name for butterbur was pestilence-wort, a stern reminder of its traditional use to produce a sweat in patients, who were treated with extracts from the roots boiled in water, a treatment which undoubtedly reduced the temperature of those afflicted with the plague, and may well have cured many. The huge umbrella-like leaves were once used to wrap butter.

In some parts of northern England the white butterbur (*Petasites albus*), introduced from Spain and the Balkans, grows well, its white flowers contrasting with the pink flowers of the native species.

Kingcup (Caltha palustris)

Although the marsh marigold or kingcup is a member of the buttercup family it has several important characteristics which warrant it being removed from the *Ranunculus* genus and placed in one of its own. It grows well in cold exposed areas and is thought to have been one of the first plants to bloom in Britain after the retreat of the ice some 10,000 years ago.

Its bright yellow-orange blooms are one of the most magnificent sights of our wetlands, often being in glorious colour as early as March, although in some upland areas it does not flower until July. The stem is thick and spongy and soon wilts if picked; this spongy texture is essential if the plant is to thrive in waterlogged areas where there will be temporary but potentially dangerous shortages of air. A close look at the flower will reveal five large shiny sepals; the petals have been reduced to small tubes, at the base of which are the nectaries which attract insects to pollinate the kingcup.

Willowherbs

> With many a curve my banks I fret
> By many a field and fallow,
> And many a fairy foreland set
> With willow-weed and mallow.

Thus wrote Tennyson in his poem *The Brook*, and around the banks of our marshlands and streams the willowherbs are the most common plants. The great hairy willowherb (*Epilobium hirsutum*) is usually the most dominant and can grow to heights of over 3 feet (1 metre). Its old country name was codlins-and-cream; codlins were a variety of apple and the name refers to the combination of pink and white found in the flowers. I find the best way to identify this flower is to examine the large stigma, which is divided into four. Also found in damp areas are the narrow leaved willowherb (*Epilobium palustre*), the square stalked willowherb (*Epilobium tetraginum*) and the small flowered willowherb (*Epilobium parviflorum*).

Ragged robin (Lychnis flos-cuculi)

This untidy-looking member of the campion family has a strangely attractive appeal. Its ragged appearance is due to the petals being deeply cut into four long segments; a close look at the flower shows that the petals are joined at the base and that both the male and female are fertile, there being ten stamens and five carpels. The latter are joined to produce a single chambered ovary, but the five styles surmounted by their stigma are clearly visible.

Marsh Woundwort (Stachys palustris)

This common plant, in bloom from June to September, had an important use when battles were fought on the flowery fields of Britain. Pushed into wounds, the leaves had the power to staunch blood and perhaps even destroy bacteria. The leaves themselves are lance shaped and are carried on a stem which can be up to a metre high (39.4 inches). It may well have been these leaves which suggested to the superstitious soldiers that God had made them lance shaped in order to indicate their function. The flowers are borne in whorls and are purple in colour.

Marsh woundwort is sometimes found growing alongside its rarer relative the skull-cap (*Scutellaria galericulata*), which also has lance-like leaves but is a much more delicate plant with delightful blue flowers. Skull-cap, which gets its name from the shape of its flowers, can grow to a height of around 50 cm (19.7 inches), while the lesser skull-cap (*Scutellaria minor*) is around 15 cm (6 inches) and distinguished also by its tiny purple flowers dotted with dark red.

A stroll along a river bank will reveal most of the species described in this chapter and also a number of others. There are few greater thrills than plant hunting along river banks. Within a short time the common species will be well known and the unusual species will then be noticed.

CHAPTER SIX

Invertebrates

A NYONE who frequents watercourses, whether rambler, angler or boater, must have wondered what lurks beneath the surface, besides the obvious fish; dipping into the water with even a makeshift net or turning over a stone in the shallows (we should all remember to return the displaced stones to their original position) will reveal another world. This chapter concerns itself with all the invertebrates (see table two) except the arthropods, which merit a chapter to themselves.

Typical representatives of each phylum will be described, although in a book of this nature there can be no comprehensive coverage and the choice is therefore subjective. Most of the animals described, however, are fairly common. I have not made any attempt to describe many microscopic forms, but have endeavoured to make amends for this in the bibliography.

Table 2. Classification of Invertebrate Animals of Fresh Water

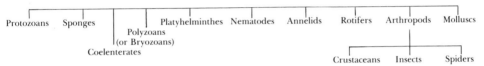

Protozoans   Sponges   Platyhelminthes   Nematodes   Annelids   Rotifers   Arthropods   Molluscs

Polyzoans (or Bryozoans)

Coelenterates

Crustaceans   Insects   Spiders

Protozoans (Protozoa)

The amoeba living in the stream and pond-side mud is a familiar animal to junior biologists, but despite its appearance in text books it is very tiny, measuring only about 0.033 cm (0.013 inches), and difficult to

An amoeba seen through the microscope.   *Alan W. Heath*

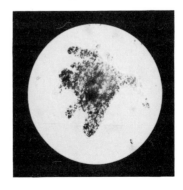

find. The Protozoa are best described as acellular rather than single celled, since this cell may be controlled by one or several nuclei, and have a complex internal organisation.

Being animals, they depend for their food directly upon plants or indirectly upon the decaying remains of larger plants and animals. A few of the larger species actively hunt those smaller than themselves, while some may live as dangerous parasites on or inside the bodies of larger organisms. One class of the Protozoa is that of the parasitic Sporozoa, which includes the human malarial parasite; another is a species called *Glugea anomala* which attacks sticklebacks. Evidence of its presence can be seen in the form of white cysts loaded with spores, which explains why infection can spread quickly.

The river watcher, however, is unlikely to encounter the usually microscopic Protozoa and this section is therefore brief.

Freshwater sponges (Porifera)

Sponges are almost entirely marine and, with the notable exception of the bath sponge, are very small and quite likely to be overlooked. Many are not recognised as sponges because they look rather like a frothy scum without an organised structure. This is true of the two British species of river sponge which are found encrusting stones or the submerged stems of aquatic plants. They are of irregular shape, the precise form being determined to a large extent by the environment. All specimens, however, will reveal small pores, each called an osculum, and each osculum connects to a canal and has a collar cell with a whip-like flagellum which drives a current of water into the sponge. This brings in oxygen and food, the waste products being carried out through the ostium, which can reverse the beat, although how this is controlled when the sponge has no recognised nervous system remains something of a mystery.

The two freshwater species are the pond sponge (*Euspongilla lacustris*) and the river sponge (*Euphydatia fluviatilis*) which are quite common in some areas. Where a specimen is found exposed to sunlight it can be bright green due to the presence of single-celled green algae belonging to the Pleurococcus family; these are only lodgers and the sponges can live perfectly well without the algae, in which case they are cream coloured.

Close examination of sponge tissue reveals a protective palisade of spicules made of calcium carbonate and silica; water lacking these essential chemicals has few, if any, specimens of sponge. If a sponge is split each section is able to generate a new specimen; this type of reproduction is obviously asexual. During the summer, however, male sponges (the sexes cannot be separated by external appearance) release into the water mobile sperms which fertilise eggs to produce larvae. These larvae, which can also move by means of beating cilia, settle down after about twelve hours to divide and produce a sponge. By autumn the young sponge is less than 2 cm (0.8 inch) in diameter, but it is able to survive until the following spring inside a protective case known as a gemmule.

Obviously the sponge is a perfect hiding place for other animals, but most do no harm to the sponge. The spongilla fly *Sisyra fuscata*, however, is a parasite; it is a species of lacewing whose larva extracts food from the tissues of the sponge.

Hydroids (Coelentera)

As with sponges, the coelenterates are predominantly marine and include the corals and jellyfish. Coelenterates are said to be radially symmetrical, having their bodies arranged around a central stem, with no head, tail or right and left sides. A radially symmetrical animal is ideally

A brown hydra fed with *Daphnia magna*.
Alan W. Heath

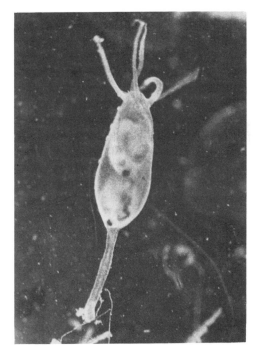

91

structured to live a sedentary life and is typically secured to stones or to a sturdy plant by a basal disc, catching food by waving tentacles, of which there are between four and twenty arranged around the mouth and waving in the current. There is only one entrance to the sac-like body, through which food captured by the tentacles is taken in and waste substances ejected. The central cavity is called the enteron.

Two layers of cells make up the body, the inner layer or endoderm dealing with the digestion of food and its absorption; the cells of the outer layer, the ectoderm, like those of the endoderm, are embedded in the jelly-like material of the mesoglea which separates the two layers. In

A green hydra, *Hydra viridissima*, seen through the microscope.
Alan W. Heath

the ectoderm there are muscle cells which allow the body to expand and contract; there are also simple nerve cells which form an efficient nerve net over the surface, but the most fascinating cells of all are the cnidoblasts, of which there are three main types. Some called volvents are smooth and wrap around the body of the prey, while the glutinants allow the coelenterates to stick to objects. These are useful if the animal wishes to detach its basal disc and shift its position. It is the so-called penetrants, however, which may well inspire science fiction writers. Like all cnidoblasts, they are concentrated in batteries on the tentacles. When these touch prey or a potential enemy (as any swimmer coming into contact with a jellyfish knows well) a sharp three-pronged barb shoots out and penetrates the tissue; the cnidoblast then contracts and squeezes a painful and paralysing poison into the wound. If prey is caught the tentacles bend over and the animal feeds by 'licking its fingers'.

The freshwater hydras can often be found secured to stones or to the leaves or stems of water plants. When disturbed they contract, but if the stones or plants are kept still for a while the creatures expand and are large enough to be seen by the naked eye, their tentacles hanging out hopefully in search of food. Although much more common in still water, they are frequently seen in slow-running rivers and ditches. A feature of all coelenterates, and of hydras in particular, is their dramatic powers of regeneration, new animals arising from each tiny section of a damaged animal. In addition to this often 'accidental' method of reproduction, hydras do develop sexual organs prior to the onset of winter, and the eggs may then be encysted until the following spring.

The microhydras are a rather uncommon genus found in running water; they lack tentacles although they have sting cells on the flexible body surface. Another fascinating coelenterate is *Cordylophora lacustris*, which is found both in estuaries and along navigable rivers all the way up to dockland areas far inland, including London. This species has obviously only recently—in evolutionary terms at least—left the sea. Its body form resembles hydra but whereas the reproductive buds formed on hydra soon detach themselves from the parent to live independent lives, those of *Cordylophora* remain attached to the parent, and substantial colonies, which are either male or female, develop.

Moss animalcules (Polyzoa)

The Polyzoa are also mainly marine animals and are often known as sea mats. There are freshwater species—about a dozen in Europe—which look superficially like hydras, a likeness which often leads to confusion. The colonies are typified by their polyp members, which have a horseshoe-shaped crown of tentacles called the lophophore. The tentacles do not possess sting cells but are ciliated (they have cilia, short hairlike processes projecting from some of the cells), and although the nervous system is primitive it is able to co-ordinate the beating cilia to drive food such as algae into the mouth. Unlike the coelenterates, each polyp has an anus through which waste products can be eliminated.

Each individual is embedded in, and connected to, other members of the colony by a strong sheath into which it can withdraw when danger threatens. The polyps are attached firmly by a structure known as a funiculus, while the ovaries are situated deep inside the housing wall; the sperms (probably from another colony) are drawn in by the feeding current. Freshwater species produce asexual statoblasts, which are buds protected by a resistant wall. Should the parent colony perish in the winter these dormant 'buds' can regenerate another colony by asexual budding.

Cristatella mucedo is perhaps the best-known species but is seldom found in rivers. Equally common is *Plumatella repens*, which is found attached to leaves and stones in streams, ditches and in the damp areas of riversides. The species is characterised by having oval-shaped statoblasts and by the branching shape of the colony, which makes it very plant-like and earns it the name of moss-animal.

Flatworms (Platyhelminthes)

Flatworms are best known for their parasitic habits, and well-documented species include the Cestoda (tapeworms) and the Trematoda (liverflukes). These are both typified by having two hosts, one of which is the major host, the other being a carrier and known as the vector. Many freshwater snails are vectors, especially of liverflukes, which can be lethal to sheep. Because of these effects on both man and his domestic animals the parasites have been much studied; the free-living flatworms are not so well known. These belong to the class Turbellaria, which derives its name from the Latin meaning a small disturbance. This disturbance is created by the cilia which cover the body surface and produce a flow of water to bring a supply of oxygen and also to remove carbon dioxide and other waste materials. The cilia can also be used for movement, and the flatworm seems to glide smoothly along. Movement is also helped by unique rod-like structures called rhabdites which break down to produce a slime which overcomes friction and is also used to entangle potential prey.

There are two orders of ciliated flatworms found in Britain, the Rhabdocoeles, found mainly in still water, and the Triclads, so named because their guts are divided into three branches. This order includes the planarians, of which twelve species are found in Britain. Planarians feed on small animals which they trap in the slime made from the rhabdites or on the dead and rotting bodies of larger animals. They can easily be attracted by baiting with meat, especially at night since planarians are mainly nocturnal. They are usually dark in colour and can be found under stones, even where the current is quite fast. They have been the subject of fascinating experiments because of their quite staggering powers of regeneration; even tiny pieces have been known to develop into complete animals. At one time there was considerable debate about whether the planarian nervous system was predominantly electrical or chemical; experiments were performed in which animals

A planarian worm, *Dendrocoelum lacteum*, which can be found under stones in many rivers, even those which are quite fast-flowing.   *John Clegg*

were taught to negotiate a simple maze. When these individuals were chopped up and fed to untrained planarians the latter soon 'digested' the lesson and moved through the maze without difficulty.

Round worms (Nematoda)

The majority of the nematodes, which are round elastic-like worms, live as parasites inside both plants and animals. There are several freshwater species which live freely in the bottom mud; they are characterised by their movement, during which the body is twisted into a smooth S shape. Individual species are, however, difficult to identify and proper identification is a job for the dedicated expert. The same applies to those found in the gut of freshwater animals, including fish; nematodes are often encountered by fishermen as the catch is gutted. Freshwater birds are seldom without gut worms, and they are often unwelcome guests in the human intestines.

Often confused with the much shorter nematodes are the Gordiaceae, of which there is one genus present in fresh water. This is the hairworm *Gordius*, which can reach up to 65 cm (25.5 inches) in length. The sexes are separated, both male and female having a thin opaque body, but the male's body is forked at the end, the female's is not. The larvae are parasitic on the bodies of mayflies, alderflies and other aquatic insects, entry being gained by means of a sharp boring apparatus situated at the head end. Eventually the larva leaves its host and the adult lives a free existence. The adult does not, however, feed, but deserves both its scientific and vernacular names. It certainly looks like a hair—indeed in

95

the old days country folk thought it was a horse hair come to life. It gets the name *Gordius* from its curled up appearance resembling a Gordian knot. Although *Gordius* is more common in stagnant water it is also found in ditches and slow-moving rivers.

True worms (Annelida)

Easily recognised by their cylindrical and segmented bodies, the annelids are true worms. The earthworm is often described as the typical species, but this is not quite accurate since many are marine and there are also important freshwater species. The latter species belong to one of two groups, the Chaetopoda, characterised by having bristles on most, if not all, the body segments, and the Hirudinea or leeches, which lack bristles and have suckers.

Bristle worms (Oligochaeta)

Anglers and naturalists searching fresh water often come across what they believe are earthworms which have 'fallen into the water by accident'. A close examination, however, will reveal that the specimen is a square tailed worm (*Eiseniella*), whose pink body is usually around 5 cm (2 inches) long with a pointed head and, as its name implies, a square tail.

Eiseniella is a common resident among the mossy stones at the head of quite turbulent rivers but others (there are five species in Britain) occur in lakes and ponds. The Tubificidae is a tube-dwelling family of bristle worm (already described in chapter one) which is able to withstand low oxygen levels due to the high concentrations of haemoglobin in its circulatory system, from which it gets its name of 'blood worm'. The animal feeds by drawing in mud and extracting nutrients as it passes through the body. The pot worms (Enchytraeidae) are a large family—possibly as many as 140 British species—which seldom exceed 2.5 cm (1 inch) in length; they are found among the algae and mosses alongside rivers, especially quickly flowing streams which splash the riverside zone and keep the plants dripping with lifegiving water. The pot worms are well versed in the art of camouflage and usually hold their pale bodies so rigid that they resemble the roots of waterside plants.

The bristle worms are hermaphrodites; when mating two animals lie side by side and produce a thick layer of slime before bringing their sex organs together. Sperms are then exchanged, because the species would not be able to improve if each individual fertilised itself. The eggs are deposited in protective cocoons which encircle the body. All the worm then has to do is to wriggle free of its reproductive belt; the offspring within it develop into adults without going through larval stages. During these early stages, and also in the adults of some species, the power of regeneration is almost as spectacular as that of the planarians. Bristle worms are unknown to all but anglers and naturalists, but this is certainly not so in the case of leeches, which are usually considered as dangerous and even loathsome creatures.

Leeches (Hirudinea)

In Britain's fresh waters there are still seventeen species of leech, more often encountered in still than in moving waters, and anyone who studies the biology of rivers will soon encounter these fascinating creatures. Leeches move by having a pair of suckers at each end of the body; first the hind sucker is attached and the segmented body is then extended by very powerful body muscles; the anterior sucker is then attached and the rear sucker relaxes its grip, allowing the body to be telescoped; the sequence can be repeated very quickly. Some leeches are also able to swim by means of sinuous loopings of the body.

Like the bristle worms, all the British species of leech are hermaphrodites; although they prefer to mate in pairs there are records of self-fertilisation occurring, which may be useful when these parasites are not found in high densities. The eggs are laid in capsules which are either buried in the mud or attached to water weeds. Some members of the family Glossiphonidae seem to show a degree of parental concern over the welfare of the young, often placing the body around the object to which the cocoon is attached and directing a current of well-oxygenated water over it by means of a fanning movement. In *Glossiphonia heteroclita* the young which hatch have adaptations on the suckers which allow them to grip the parent; it would be wrong to refer to a hermaphrodite as the mother. All leeches feed upon animal material, some being carnivores which rip the food, often larger than themselves, to pieces; others are bloodsuckers. Several species are found in running water.

Piscicola geometra

This greenish-yellow species, which grows up to 5 cm (2 inches) and feeds on the blood of freshwater fish, prefers well-oxygenated water and is therefore found even in the upper reaches of rivers. The cylindrical body has a particularly prominent anterior sucker. The cocoons are cemented to the undersides of sheltered stones, to which the adults may also attach themselves when waiting for potential prey. When the opportunity arises they fasten on to the fish's body, especially the area around the gills where the blood supply is likely to be closest to the surface.

Glossiphonia complanata

Varying in size from 1.5 cm to 3.5 cm (0.6 inches to 1.34 inches), this species has an obviously flattened body and the anterior sucker is no wider than the segments behind it; this head sucker is not visible from above. There are usually three pairs of eyes, though in the occasional specimen the first pair of eyes is less obvious than the other two pairs and may be missing altogether. The number and distribution of the eyes in leeches has been used by Helen Mellanby and others (see bibliography) as the main distinguishing feature.

Glossiphonia complanata has an almost translucent greenish-brown body with two often-interrupted lines along its dorsal surface. It is not particularly active and soon contracts its body into a ball if disturbed. It is very common, being found in both still and running water, usually feeding on bloodworms but also upon the body fluids of gastropods (see molluscs below). While waiting for prey it conceals itself under stones to avoid being disturbed by the current.

Glossiphonia heteroclita is a closely related amber-coloured species found in slow-moving rivers and ponds, but it apparently prefers soft waters. Another distinguishing feature is the presence of small brownish-black spots on the dorsal surface. It is smaller than *G. complanata* and seldom exceeds 1.5 cm (0.6 inch). Unlike the former species *G. heteroclita* is rare in Ireland and has not been recorded in Scotland. Both species produce gelatinous cocoons which are carried on the dorsal surface of the parent's body until the food reserves in the eggs have become exhausted. Like the bristle worms, leeches do not have a larval stage, the young looking like tiny versions of the parents.

Theromyzon tessulatum

This interesting species is found in the mouths and nasal passages of waterfowl. It often occurs in numbers large enough to cause substantial blood loss, and this may be a factor in the death of many ducks along rivers and canals and in ponds. The species is absent from the fast-moving headstreams of rivers, but is able to lie in wait for a potential host under stones in areas of quite rapid water movement. It is greenish in colour and has six rows of yellowish spots along its back. There are four pairs of eyes. The reproductive behaviour is rather inconsistent, with the egg capsules sometimes being carried on the underside of the parent, while other individuals attach them to submerged objects.

Holobdella stagnalis

Despite its name this species is very common in slow-moving rivers and streams, especially those in chalk and limestone districts where the water is hard. The body, which is pale grey but translucent and occasionally tinged with green, is leaf shaped and varies from 1 cm to 2.5 cm (0.4 inch to 1 inch), with most animals being in the smaller range. The anterior sucker is narrower than the segments behind it and cannot be seen from above; and the dorsal surface has black spots, although there is no definite arrangement. It appears to the author that the patterning of spots is unique to the individual leech. There is only one pair of eyes in this species and the eyes are placed very close together. *Holobdella stagnalis* feeds on other annelids, being particularly fond of bloodworms.

Horse leech (Haemopsis sanguisuga)

The fact that it has a vernacular name means that this large species, which sometimes reaches a length of 15 cm (5.9 inches), was well known to countryfolk of old. They believed that seven leeches of this species could suck the blood out of a horse and leave it a shrivelled corpse. It is certainly true that the animal does look formidable when fully expanded, its black dorsal surface adding to its sinister appearance, but in fact the horse leech never sucks blood but feeds on earthworms, snails and insect larvae as well as the tadpoles of amphibians. It is also not averse to eating the weaker members of its own species.

The powerful jaws have been examined and found to have as many as eighteen pairs of tooth-like organs which rasp away at the larger prey like a file; smaller animals are swallowed whole. These 'teeth', despite rumours to the contrary, cannot penetrate human skin or the thick hide of a horse. There are five pairs of eyes.

The horse leech is common throughout Britain and is often found on riversides moving about by means of its suckers. It deposits cocoons in damp soil as well as on stones in the river itself.

Erpobdella octoculata

This species is a narrowly elongated species around 4 cm (1.6 inch) when at rest under stones and sheltered from the current. The colour of the dorsal surface is dark brown and with even darker markings, but the ventral surface is lighter. There are four pairs of eyes. Its food is obtained by nocturnal hunting; included in the diet are planarians and insect larvae. The fact that it also feeds upon bloodworms means that it can exist even in areas of quite high pollution. The cocoons of eggs are of a flattened oval shape and are carefully attached by the parent to the undersides of stones.

Wheel animalcules (Rotifera)

These very tiny creatures, often confused with protozoa, are found on close examination to have bodies made up of many cells. Confusion is caused by the lack of clearly defined cell walls and so the groups of jelly-like body cells together called syncytia appear as a multi-nucleated mass. Rotifers seldom exceed .025 cm (0.01 inch) and so they need to be hunted with net and microscope, some species being almost continuously

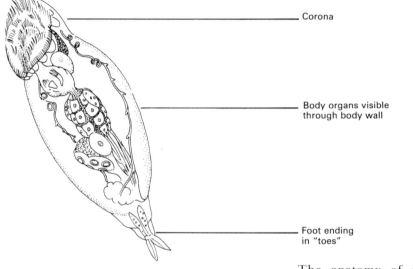

Corona

Body organs visible
through body wall

Foot ending
in "toes"

The anatomy of a rotifer,
Epiphones.

attached to water weeds while others are free swimming, such species obviously being restricted to slow-moving or still water.

There are several marine species, but by far the majority of the 1,500 species (of which around 300 occur in Britain) are found in fresh water. Some species are able to live in damp moss or soil and a few live as parasites. Both the scientific name of Rotifer and the vernacular name of wheel animals refer to the complex organ at the anterior of the animal by which they move and feed. This structure, the corona, is made up of long cilia which vibrate to produce movement and to set up currents of water carrying food, also a means of respiratory exchange. In a minority of the rotifers the corona may be reduced or absent altogether; its varying shape is used by biologists to separate one species from another.

Another feature of the rotifers is the anterior stalk, often called the foot, a description which seems even more apt as it ends in two 'toes'. The whirling wheels at the front and the twinkling toes at the rear, which also help in locomotion, ensure that rotifers are much sought after by amateur microscopists.

The reproduction of rotifers is unusual, since for most of the time the males are either degenerate or absent altogether, the females reproducing parthenogenetically. Even when males do fertilise the females the procedure is unusual; sperm is introduced to the female ovary by means of a sharp stylus which can only penetrate the female when she is young and her body wall is soft. Fertilisation is therefore a once-only event, and the sperm is stored to be used when required. The eggs when laid are often resistant to drought; thus the wheel animals are able to overcome the adverse conditions which result from stretches of water drying up.

Molluscs (Mollusca)

The molluscs represent the second largest phylum or basic division in the animal kingdom; there may well be as many as 100,000 species still alive today. They are thought to have arisen in the sea, and it is in this habitat that all four classes of mollusc are found. There are the Polyplacophora (chitons or coat-of-mail shells), Bivalvia (the bivalves), Gastropoda (slugs and snails) and the Cephalopoda (the squids and octopuses). Only the bivalves and gastropods, often called univalves since the shell consists of one unit, are found in fresh water. In Britain there are twenty-eight species of freshwater mussel (bivalves) and thirty-six freshwater snails (univalves); despite the obvious differences in the shells they have many typical molluscan features in common.

Molluscs are bilaterally symmetrical, the soft bodies (mollusc means soft body) packed into a dorsal hump called the visceral mass and covered by a skin called the epidermis. This, usually referred to as the pallium or mantle, extends along the ventral surface to form a foot. A mantle cavity is isolated between the foot and the head and the body wall. Gills and even primitive lungs can develop in this space and provide an efficient respiratory surface. In some molluscs—the bivalves and univalves—the mantle secretes a shell formed from a basic matrix of a protein called conchiolin, which is impregnated and reinforced usually with calcium carbonate. This means that hard waters tend to be richer in molluscs than areas of soft water. Many shells are lined with mother-of-pearl, also called nacre, which consists of blocks of aragonite, a form of calcium carbonate. Pearls are formed when particles of silt or sand enter the shell and irritate the mantle cavity, thus stimulating the mollusc to secrete nacre around it and so produce a pearl (see below).

Freshwater bivalves

The ideal habitat for freshwater molluscs is unpolluted, hard, gently flowing river with an abundant supply of water plants ensuring high concentrations of oxygen as a result of their photosynthetic activities. The freshwater bivalves are related to marine oysters, mussels and cockles, the two valves or shells being formed from the mantle, hinged and closed by the powerful adductor muscles, one set at each end of the shell.

Swan mussel (Anodonta cygnea)

This powerful species can have a shell up to 22 cm (8.66 inches) long and is common in most large stretches of hard fresh water, including the slower stretches of river. In south-western England and Scotland it seems to be less common or even absent. The large, thin shell is smooth, glossy and brown in appearance, due to a thin brown epidermis which peels off from the shells of dead specimens to reveal a greenish yellow colour. A full-grown specimen is thought to be some fourteen years old.

They must have been exploited as juicy food supplies as well as for the occasional pearl; it is known that the Romans had pearl fisheries along several British rivers including the Esk at Ravenglass in Cumbria and Lancashire's Ribble. Like many bivalves, *Anodonta cygnea* has limited movement, effected by its muscular foot and also by opening and closing of the valves.

It does not need to move since it can control its own environment by drawing in a current of water through its ciliated inhalent siphon and pumping out a current via the exhalent siphon. The water entering contains microscopic animals which are trapped in the slimy surface of two large organs called gills. Another group of beating co-ordinated cilia drive the slime and the food towards the mouth. Oxygen is extracted all over the gill surface and waste gases can also be got rid of in this area.

The siphons are also important in the reproduction of the swan mussel. The male releases his sperm via his exhalent siphon; these are drawn into the body of the female to fertilise her eggs, which are retained in the outer folds of her mantle until they hatch into tiny *glochidia* larvae, which are recognisable bivalves at this stage, able to hang on to the parent's gills by tiny tooth-like projections. Eventually after about nine months the *glochidia* escape via the exhalent siphon and lie in wait, usually attached to water plants, until approached by a fish. They then attach themselves to the fish and live on it parasitically for a while before detaching themselves and living an independent life. Thus the fish both provides food and acts as a method of molluscan dispersal.

Duck mussel (Anodonta anatina)

This species tends to occur in faster rivers than the swan mussel, especially when there is a sandy bottom into which the duck mussel can burrow. At one time conchologists thought it was merely a sub-species of the swan mussel but the smaller duck mussel, which measures around 9 cm (3.5 inches), is now considered a species in its own right. The shell is

| Planorbis | Limnaea | Anodonta |

The basic shapes of three common freshwater molluscs.   *Carole Pugh*

thicker than that of the swan mussel and it is also darker in colour and more oval in shape. *Anodonta anatina* has a similar lifestyle to that of its larger relative, but tends to be less common in southern Britain but much more common in the North, especially Scotland.

Pearl mussel (Margaritifera margaritifera)

The pearl mussel seems able to build its shell from chemicals extracted from fairly soft water. It is found in deep, fast-moving rivers flowing through areas of south-western and north-western Britain which are not particularly hard, where it survives well by growing in colonies in deep areas protected by boulders on the river bed. The shell dimensions are about 13.5 cm long and 6.8 cm wide (5.3 inches × 2.7 inches), the thickish oval shell being dark brown in colour. The inner surface of the shell is richly supplied with nacre, which is why the species can occasionally produce magnificent pearls. In Ireland some workers have suggested that *Margaritifera durrovensis* might well be a separate species which favours hard water, but until it is found in other rivers besides the Nore some would consider this to be an ambitious claim.

Painter's mussel (Unio pictorum)

The long narrow shells of the painter's mussel can reach almost 13 cm (5 inches) in length and were commonly used as vessels for mixing paints. The average length is around 10 cm (4 inches) and the width is

4 cm (1.6 inch), the toothed appearance of the hinge of the shell being diagnostic. It prefers slow-flowing rivers but is especially common in canals, particularly those in hard water districts. The species is found

Left: A painter's mussel. **Right:** The siphon of a painter's mussel.   *Alan W. Heath*

throughout England and Wales but does not occur in either Scotland or Ireland.

Zebra mussel (Dreissena polymorpha)

The zebra mussel, whose shell is about 5 cm (2 inches) long, was not too long ago a marine species and was first found in the fresh waters of Britain in 1824. It is now widespread in rivers and canals as well as in reservoirs and water mains, its zig-zag bands of brown and yellow making it easily recognisable. It is able to secure itself to roots and stones and even to the keels of boats by sticky secretions from the foot known as byssus threads, which are typical of marine species such as the edible mussel (*Mytilus edulis*). The mode of reproduction is also similar to marine species, the free-swimming larvae feeding on food particles and not having a parasitic stage. Once mature, the mussel settles down and becomes almost sedentary, feeding and respiring from the siphon currents as already described.

Pea mussel (Pisidium amnicum)

Found frequently in unpolluted streams and rivers, providing the water is hard, this species seldom exceeds 1 cm (0.4 inch) long or 0.7 cm (0.28 inch) in width. It has well-developed hinge teeth and appears to have only one siphon, but on close examination the two are seen to be fused into a single strong protective case. Altogether there are around sixteen species of *Pisidium*, some of which are widespread, including *P. amaicum*, the largest species. There are some which favour soft waters; *P. nitidum* is such a species, while *P. personatum*, recognised by its reddish shell, is able to thrive in ditches and ponds often with high levels of faecal pollution.

Orb mussel (Sphaerium corneum)

The thin-walled round swollen shell of the well-named orb mussel is around 1 cm (0.4 inch) high and is almost the same in width. The shell is yellow-brown in colour and 'teeth' are present on the hinge. Another obvious feature is the two long siphons which are easily visible when the animal is not disturbed. The method of reproduction is fascinating; each individual is an hermaphrodite and the young do not go through the parasitic stage but betray their marine connections by having byssus threads by which they attach themselves to stones and plants.

Freshwater univalves—the snails or gastropod molluscs

The gastropod molluscs have their stomachs situated in the foot and as they glide along they use their rough radula* to scrape food from rocks or to grind up water plants. Some species are able to rasp at the bodies of dead animals. In fresh water there are thirty-six species, some of which are able to tolerate life even in fast-moving rivers, although other species are confined to still waters. Gastropods can be classified into the pulmonates, which breathe atmospheric air through a quite efficient lung, and the operculates, which employ gills to remove oxygen from solution. Pulmonates, because of their ability to use atmospheric air, are less affected by pollution than the operculates. Some gastropods, such as the ramshorn snail (*Planorbis planorbis*), for example, possess haemoglobin which increases the oxygen-carrying capacity.

Pulmonates

It is thought that the pulmonates originated from land-based ancestors. They are hermaphrodites, in contrast to the operculates, which have the sexes separate, but they exchange sperm and thus self-fertilisation is prevented. There are examples of pond snails unable to find a mate which have fertilised their own eggs. The tentacles, which are triangular in shape, are not retractile and each has an eye close to its base.

Ramshorn snails. Also called trumpet snails because of the shape of the shell, the ramshorn snails can live in both still and flowing water; there

*A short broad strip of membrane bearing rows of chitinous teeth.

are fourteen species found in fresh water. Their blood contains haemoglobin and therefore looks red; normally the blood of molluscs is blue due to the presence of the copper-based haemocyanin. Albino forms sometimes occur; they look really beautiful as the red colour can be seen through the shell. Two of the most likely species to be found in rivers are the great ramshorn (*Planorbis corneum*) and the common ramshorn (*Planorbis planorbis*). There has been a tendency in recent years to prefer the scientific name of *Planorbarius corneus* for the former species, which can be 1 cm (0.4 inch) high and 0.25 cm (0.1 inch) in breadth. The shell is twisted into five or six whorls and is dark brown and glossy. The

A great ramshorn snail, *Planorbis corneum,* a mollusc which is often found in rivers, particularly those containing hard water. *John Clegg*

soft-bodied animal within is brownish red. Hard waters are preferred, and this factor is more likely to affect distribution than whether the water is still or moving.

All the planorbid snails seem to have lived in fresh water longer than the pond snails (see below), and part of the mantle has been modified as a secondary gill. The great ramshorn seems to be more common in the South of Britain than it is in the North. *Planorbis planorbis*, which has a duller surface and is only 0.3 cm (0.12 inch) high and 1.4 cm (0.55 inch) broad, favours small stretches of water such as ditches. *Planorbis carinatus*, the keeled trumpet snail, which is the same size but has a thinner, flatter and much more glossy shell, occurs in more substantial rivers and canals but is not so often found in Scotland as the former species. The tiny *Planorbis vortex*, the whirlpool trumpet snail, has a thin, flat disc of a shell which is only 0.15 cm (0.06 inch) high and 0.8 cm (0.3 inch) broad with six or seven whorls. It is found in hard running water, especially where there are water weeds, and I have found it frequently in areas of river dominated by the water crowfoots. Looked at under a binocular microscope this species looks truly beautiful, as does the even smaller *Planorbis crista*, which is only 0.05 cm (0.02 inch) high and 0.2 cm (0.08 inch) broad, and is found among water plants in both still and running water. This species can easily be recognised by the majority of the specimens having obvious ridges on the three or four whorls of the shell.

Pond snails. The best-known species is the great pond snail (*Lymnaea stagnalis*) which has an easily recognised spiral shell tapering to a height of around 5 cm (2 inches); it is around 2.5 cm (1 inch) wide and has seven or eight whorls. It prefers hard water and despite its name is frequently encountered among the vegetation of rivers as well as in ponds. Unlike many snails, this species is something of a scavenger and will eat dead, decaying animals and occasionally will attack living fish and amphibians.

Although the *Lymnaea* snails are well adapted to life in water they still breathe atmospheric air and are obliged to visit the surface to fill their lung, which when full of air may well render them more buoyant. Other species include the widely distributed *Lymnaea palustris* or marsh snail, which frequents ditches and has a strong brown shell of six or seven whorls, being about 1.9 cm (0.75 inch) high and 0.9 cm (0.35 inch) broad. The even smaller *Lymnaea truncatula* is only 0.8 cm (0.31 inch) high and 0.4 cm (0.157 inch) broad but is, like the marsh snail, more of an agricultural pest than other snails. It also occurs in ditches, ponds and in damp grass around upland rivers, where it is surprisingly resistant to temporary droughts. These two species are the intermediate hosts of the

A great pond snail, *Lymnaea stagnalis*, showing the foot and mouth.　　　　*John Clegg*

liver fluke (*Fasciola hepatica*) which spends its adult life in the sheep, often causing the death of valuable stock.

Lymnaea peregra, the wandering snail, is the commonest freshwater snail in Britain and occurs in all aquatic habitats. Its precise identification does require experience as well as skill, since the shell shape varies according to the external factors it has to face. The shell is around 2 cm (0.78 inch) high and 1.3 cm (0.5 inch) wide and is usually quite thin, having four or five whorls. The colour is yellowish brown and the spire is

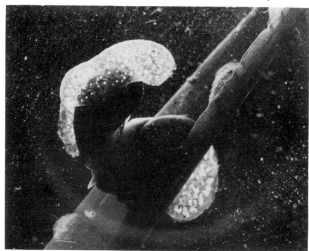

The eggs of the wandering snail, *Lymnaea peregra.*
Alan W. Heath

usually not pointed although there are variations according to habitat. Another species worth looking out for in slow-moving rivers is *Lymnaea auricularia,* the eared snail, easily identified by its ear-shaped aperture and also by its sharply pointed spire, by which it can always be distinguished from the sometimes similar wandering snail. The shell is thin and very glossy, often reaching 3.5 cm (1.4 inch) in height.

Freshwater limpets. Two species occur in Britain, the river limpet (*Ancylus fluviatilis*) and the lake limpet (*Acroloxus lacustris*). Limpets are easily distinguished from the rest of the pulmonates since they have no whorls on their shell and the apex is blunt and tilted. The river limpet is more common than the pond species, but although both are pulmonates they seem to be able to remain permanently attached to stones and have enough dissolved oxygen trapped beneath the shell to avoid having to rise to breathe. Like their marine namesakes they do indeed stick 'like limpets' and are very difficult to remove from their stones without damaging the shells.

Operculates

This sub-class is characterised by the possession of a plate called the operculum attached to its foot. When this muscular organ is withdrawn tightly into the shell the operculum acts as an effective plug. Freshwater operculates have a gill attached to the mantle and therefore do not require a lung and can remain permanently submerged. Apart from one family, the Valvatidae, the operculates have separate sexes and in many cases the female retains the fertilised eggs until they have developed and hatched, the young snails being born alive.

Basic shapes of four more common fresh-water molluscs.   *Carole Pugh*

Valvata

Viviparus fasciatus

Pisidium

Viviparus

Freshwater winkles. Freshwater winkles of the genus *Viviparus* occur in British rivers, having a distinct preference for hard waters. *Viviparus contectus* is rather smaller and less common than *Viviparus viviparus*, which as its name implies gives birth to its young alive—often as many as fifty at a time. The shell of *V. viviparus* is 4 cm (1.58 inch) and 3.2 cm (1.26 inch) broad, some 0.4 cm (0.16 inch) larger in both dimensions than *V. contectus*. They both have six or seven whorls, but the shell of *V. viviparus* is dull and that of *V. contectus* is very glossy. The method of feeding is by filtering food by means of cilia, a method not often employed by snails.

Nerite (Theodoxus fluviatilis). There can be few water snails more beautiful than the nerite, which is a mere 0.6 cm (0.24 inch) in height and 1.1 cm (0.43 inch) broad. The shell varies a great deal in colour, which has made it popular with collectors, but the basic colour is yellow-brown, ornamented by attractive oval purple markings. The nerite likes the water to be reasonably hard and is particularly common in rivers with a wide zone of fringing vegetation. The reddish operculum looks and feels quite 'limy'. It is widely distributed in England but appears to be absent from Devon and Cornwall. *Theodoxus* is the only British species found in fresh water of a very ancient molluscan family which had its origins in the primitive seas.

Jenkins' spire shell (Potamopyrgus jenkinsi). This tiny shell is only 0.5 cm (0.2 inch) high and 0.3 cm (0.12 inch) broad but after a period in estuarine waters it has become so common in rivers that it is among the first species to be noted. It was almost certainly introduced into Britain in the nineteenth century and was officially added to the estuarine fauna in 1889. Its spread may have been assisted by the fact that it is parthenogenetic (only one male specimen has ever been identified) and it is also viviparous—a very rare combination in molluscs and much more typical of insects such as the aphids (greenfly). Jenkins' spire shell belongs to the family Hydrobiidae that also includes *Hydrobia ulvae*, which is about the same size as the species under discussion and is an important item in the diet of many estuarine birds, including the shelduck (*Tadorna tadorna*). I wonder whether the rapid spread of Jenkins' spire shell may be due to its being carrried on the feet of birds, especially wildfowl.

Valve shells. Hermaphrodites are not usually found in the operculates and in this sense the three freshwater species of operculate are interesting. *Valvata piscinalis* has a small top-shaped shell measuring only 0.6 cm (0.24 inch) high and the same width, and having four or four-and-a-half whorls. It seems to prefer soft flowing water but is less common in the North of Scotland than elsewhere. *Valvata cristata* is much smaller but is widely distributed among water plants of soft flowing rivers, also occurring in ponds and canals. It is only 0.1 cm (0.04 inch) high and 0.3 cm (0.12 inch) broad, which means that the shell is distinctly disc-shaped. *Valvata cristata* has been confused with the pulmonate ramshorn snails, but the presence of the operculum quickly identifies it. The third species, *Valvata macrostoma*, has a pronounced spire, is about the same dimensions as *V. cristata*, but is still confined to ditches and the odd sluggish stream in southern England.

This chapter has perhaps attempted the impossible, for a coverage of so many invertebrate phyla in so small a space is bound to be superficial. For those who wish to have a living portrait of a river's wildlife the attempt is worthwhile. If it has whetted the reader's appetite, especially if they are anglers or better still budding conservationists, then the chapter will have served its purpose. One phylum of invertebrates was, however, omitted, and the arthropods are the subject of the following chapter.

CHAPTER SEVEN

The Arthropods

ARTHROPODS are segmented animals with jointed legs, from which the name of the phylum itself derives. Their toughened exoskeleton is made of thick chitinous cuticle. The phylum is divided into three sub-phyla, the crustaceans, insects and arachnids, which includes the mites and the spiders. These three classes are easily separated by the number of their legs; insects have three pairs, the arachnids four pairs, and the crustaceans always more than four pairs.

Crustaceans

The word crustacean derives from the the Latin word *crusta*, meaning a shell. There are more than 31,000 species of crustaceans in the world, which most authorities divide into seven classes (see table three). They dominate both marine and freshwater. This accounts for the fact that crustaceans are often given the status of a sub-phylum within the arthropods rather than being separated as a class. There will always be frustrating conflicts of taxonomic opinion which serve to keep biologists on their toes.

Table 3. Classification of Crustacea

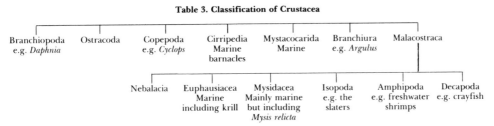

Branchiopoda

The legs of the branchiopods, perhaps better referred to as appendages, are flattened and rather leaf-like in structure. The inner-most joint of each appendage functions as a gill, from which the name of the class derives. These act not only as organs of respiration and movement but also filter food from the water. There are two body forms of the branchiopods. One form, typified by *Daphnia*, the water flea, has a short compact body in which segmentation is difficult to see; neither are

111

the appendages very easy to see. The other form, typified by *Chirocephalus*, the fairy shrimp, has an elongated body which is clearly divided into segments and has obvious limbs. This species, found in temporary pools and usually restricted to southern England, is not likely to be found by the river-based naturalist. *Daphnia*, however, is very common indeed and is often collected at the same time as the rotifers described in chapter six.

Water fleas (Daphnia)

There are around 300 species of water flea, grouped into the sub-class Cladocera. They are not very large and the commonest species, *Daphnia pulex*, is only about 0.4 cm (0.16 inch) across. Although a

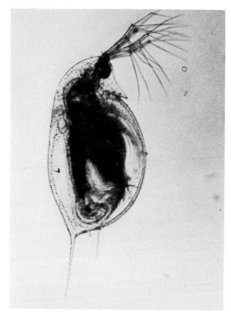

Daphnia hyalina.   *Alan W. Heath*

microscope is needed to see the fascinating detail of the body organs, *Daphnia* can be instantly recognised by its jerking movements. Many individuals are collected when a net is swept across the slow-moving areas of rivers, canals, lakes and ponds.

The head of *Daphnia* protudes forwards and bears two pairs of antennae, the second pair being much longer than the first. These are used to 'row' the animal upwards in a series of jerks. There is then a period of rest during which *Daphnia* sinks, this movement being slowed by the antennae which now spread out and function rather like a parachute. Also typical of *Daphnia* is a single compound eye called the nauplius, which evolved by the fusion of two ancestral eyes.

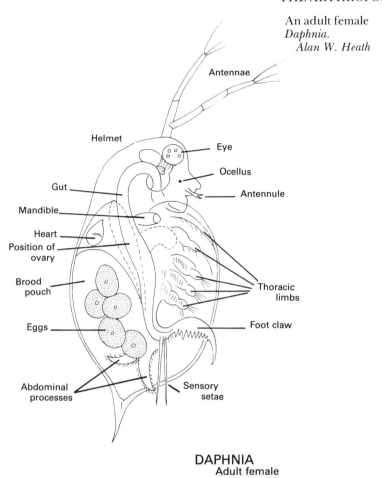

An adult female
Daphnia.
Alan W. Heath

Antennae

Helmet

Eye

Ocellus

Gut

Antennule

Mandible

Heart

Position of
ovary

Brood
pouch

Thoracic
limbs

Eggs

Foot claw

Abdominal
processes

Sensory
setae

DAPHNIA
Adult female

The shell which covers the body is called the carapace; this protective structure is transparent, and all the body organs, including the beating heart, can be seen through it. The mode of reproduction of branchiopods is often parthenogenetic; the majority of *Daphnia* populations are likely to be self-replicating females. The young females are carried in their mother's brood pouch which she tows behind her. These unfertilised eggs are thin shelled, but in adverse conditions thicker shelled eggs are produced which need to be fertilised. The male therefore adds his genes to the pool, preventing in-breeding and the potential problems likely to result from it. The fertilised eggs are produced in pairs and passed into the brood pouch. During the moult which follows fertilisation

113

the brood pouch thickens and forms a protective box which protects the eggs until external conditions, particularly temperature, improve. It is mainly females which hatch from these eggs and their parthenogenetic activities quickly build up the population, which plays such an important role in the aquatic food chains. Their own food consists of microscopic algae and animals filtered from the water by the vigorous action of the limbs, while they themselves are fed upon by larger organisms.

Ostracoda

The name of this class derives from the Greek word *ostracon*, which means either a tile or a shell, both meanings being accurate. There are over 2,000 species of ostracods of which almost seventy per cent are marine, the rest occurring in fresh water. Most of the latter are found in the mud at the bottom of ponds and are not too common in rivers, but they do occur in the lagoons of ox-bows and also in backwaters and drainage ditches. The carapace is hinged in the middle and bears a superficial resemblance to a small bivalve mollusc, but most ostracods seldom exceed 0.2 cm (0.07 inch). The genus *Cypria* is probably the best known, often occurring in huge numbers in weedy areas, the eggs being attached to the stems of water plants. This is not usual among crustaceans, which tend to carry their eggs around with them. They do, however, produce parthenogenetic eggs, the few males only becoming important when conditions deteriorate. The body is much more opaque than that of *Daphnia*, but the body can be seen to be segmented and, including the antennae, there are seven pairs of appendages. These help to sweep food particles, mainly decaying organic matter, into the mouth.

Copepoda

More than 7,500 species of copepod inhabit the waters of the world and they are important in both freshwater and marine food chains. In Europe there are only around forty freshwater forms belonging to three sub-orders, the Calanoidea, Harpacticoidea and Cyclopoidea, which includes the *Cyclops* genus. The word copepod has Greek roots—kope means an oar and pod means a foot. Copepods have no shell and have a pear-shaped body clearly segmented and divided into thorax and abdomen. The pear shape is particularly obvious in the bodies of the *Cyclops* genus found in all types of freshwater and also in brackish areas. They are typified by a single nauplius eye and a pair of egg sacs which hang from the body.

Cyclops propel themselves through the water by rowing movements of the head appendages as in *Daphnia* but assisted to some extent by the thoracic appendages. There are no appendages on any abdominal

A female *Cyclops* with egg-sacs.   *John Clegg*

segment except the last, which bears the tail fan, called the telson. Female cyclops outnumber the males and are much larger. Coupling takes place in all but the coldest months of the year, the male fastening on the female; as he is carried along he deposits two structures called spermatophores on to the female spermatheca, situated on her seventh thoracic segment. Fertilisation is internal, each female carrying sufficient sperm to father several batches of eggs, which are transferred to ovisacs. The eggs can hatch at any time between twelve hours and five days, depending upon temperature. The larva is called a nauplius because of the characteristic median eye. After six moults it begins to resemble the adult, without a complete set of thoracic segments and an unsegmented abdomen. A further five moults are required before the adult cyclops emerges.

Branchiura

The Branchiura is a class of around eighty species of bloodsucking ectoparasites preying upon amphibians and fish, being particularly fond of the latter. Several modifications in body structure have been necessary in order to hold on to the skin or the inside of the gill cover of a fish; the

115

first pair of antennae have evolved into claws, and suckers have also developed at the bases of the first maxillae (mouth parts). The appendages on the thorax are well developed, and are used by the branchiurans to move from one host to another.

The best-known British examples are the dish-shaped members of the *Argulus* genus, which are usually referred to as the fish lice. At one time they were classed with the copepods but are now thought worthy of their own class status. *Argulus foliaceus* is very common on many species of

Argulus filiaceus.
Carole Pugh

freshwater fish, its flattened body being equipped with suckers and offering so little resistance to the water that even swift currents and sudden movements fail to dislodge it. The animals are almost transparent, especially so in the case of the males. There is a poison spine sited between the two ventral suckers, but it is not certain whether this can partially immobilise the host while the sharp jaws of *Argulus* rasp away at the flesh until the blood runs freely. The males, which are rather smaller than their mates, are able to fertilise the females either when they are swimming freely or attached to a host. *Argulus foliaceus* females are 0.6 cm (0.25 inch) across; there is a rather larger but much less common species, *Argulus coregoni*, often referred to as the carp louse.

Malacostraca

This class contains the larger crustaceans and is divided into six orders (see table three), each of which will be considered briefly, the stress obviously being placed on species commonly found in fresh water in general and rivers in particular.

The Nebalacia is a primitive marine order not found in fresh water; they live in the muddy sediments beneath shallow seas. The Euphausiacea are also marine, but the members are free swimming and include the abundant krill which are so important in the marine food chains. The Mysidacea are free swimming, having a delicately thin carapace and an elongated abdomen. *Mysis relicta* is a cold water species found in seas but also in mountain streams, but unlikely to be encountered in British rivers. This leaves us with the Isopoda, Amphipoda and Decapoda, which are particularly common in the sea but are also important in freshwater ecology.

Isopoda

More usually known as slaters, and sometimes incorrectly as lice, the *Isopoda* are abundantly represented in both sea and freshwater. The woodlice are able to exist on land providing they remain under stones or leaf litter so that the body surface is kept moist. There are six freshwater species including *Asellus aquaticus* and the similar but less common *Asellus meridianus*. *Asellus aquaticus* is larger, often reaching almost 2.5 cm (1 inch), and is darker in colour; the antennae are almost as long as the body, while in *Asellus meridianus* they do not exceed two-thirds of the body length. The body is flattened dorso-ventrally, enabling them to slide into tiny spaces under stones and among the stems of water plants. *Asellus* is surprisingly tolerant of pollution in both moving and still water and feeds

A slater, *Asellus*, which feeds on decaying vegetable matter and is itself food for both fishes and birds.
John Clegg

on decaying vegetable matter. The animal itself is eaten by fish and birds, including dipper, grey wagtail and common sandpiper.

It is large enough to be turned over so that its nineteen pairs of limbs can be examined. There are two pairs of antennae used to investigate the environment, four pairs of mouth parts, seven pairs of delicate limbs on the thorax, which are used for movement, and six pairs of abdominal limbs. The first five of these bear broad gills which are used in respiration. Adult slaters are dark grey-green, but some individuals, especially young specimens, are colourless, and the body organs can be seen through the shell. Blood can often be seen flowing and the heart, situated dorsally as in all invertebrates, can be observed beating.

In *Asellus aquaticus* (but not in *A. meridianus*) the male carries the female around with him, which appears to stimulate her to lay eggs, often as early as late February but usually in April or May. The eggs are carried in a white bag under the head on the ventral surface, the young being released when they are capable of fending for themselves.

Amphipoda

In contrast to the isopods, amphipods are flattened from side to side and therefore swim on their sides. Despite their name freshwater shrimps, the amphipods are not related to shrimps; the best example is

Freshwater shrimp. *Carole Pugh*

Gammarus pulex, which was described in chapter two. They are related to the sandhoppers found among the damp seaweeds thrown up on to beaches by high tides. These are *Gammarus daubeni*, *Gammarus zaddachi* and *Gammarus chevreuxi*.

Decapoda

Economically the decapods are the most important order of crustaceans, including lobsters, crabs, prawns and shrimps. The only species to be found regularly in freshwater is the crayfish (*Astacus pallipes*), which was described in chapter two.

Insects

Insects are typified by having adult forms with segmented bodies divided into three regions, the head, thorax and abdomen. Each of the three thoracic segments bears one pair of five-jointed legs. The primitive insects (sub-class Apterygota) do not have wings in the adult stage and are therefore separated from the sub-class Pterygota which have wings at some time in the life history. Altogether taxonomists recognise twenty-three orders of insect, of which eleven are represented in the freshwaters of Britain (see table four).

Table 4.

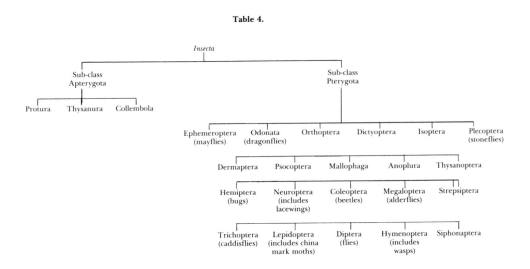

Mayflies (Ephemeroptera)

Some aspects of mayfly biology have already been discussed in chapter two. All species are characterised by two pairs of gauze-like wings, although the hind pair are very small; when at rest the wings are held vertically over the body. A unique feature of mayfly development is their ability to undergo one more moult after flight has been achieved. It is these juicy sub-imagos of the mayfly which 'rise' from the water and settle on vegetation or riverbank walls before moulting into their short-lived breeding skin.

Dragonflies (Odonata)

Few insects in or around water create more interest or generate more fear than 'horse stingers', as dragonflies were known to the old countryfolk. 'Devil's darning needle' was another descriptive vernacular name. It is equally true to say that no insects are so misunderstood as the dragonflies, which feed by catching flying insects in a 'basket' formed by holding the first pair of thoracic legs together and are unable to sting. The adults have two pairs of well-developed wings enabling them to fly much more efficiently than their prey. The veining on the wings shows a

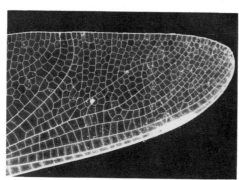

Left: A dragonfly's wing, with its intricate pattern of veining.   *Alan W. Heath*

Opposite: A close-up of a dragonfly showing the compound eyes. *Robert Howe*

system of intricate patterning which is used to classify the different species.

The head bears a pair of huge compound eyes made up of as many as 25,000 separate facets, enabling the dragonfly to build up a sort of jig-saw picture. The abdomen is long and often pointed, thus accounting for the old assertion that they carried a lethal sting.

In the world there are around 4,500 species, some large and magnificently coloured; in Europe there are only about 130, while we in Britain have only forty-four species. Some of these are threatened, and three have actually become extinct since 1945. These are *Coenagrion scitulum*, *Coenagrion armatum*, which failed to survive the draining of part of the Norfolk Broads, and *Oxygastra curtisii*, which was destroyed in its last refuge by the effluent released from a sewage farm on the West Moor River in Hampshire.

Many other species are threatened by loss of essential habitat, sometimes due to the lowering of the water table as drainage systems are initiated with scant if any thought for the majority of the wildlife. If in the present partially conservation-minded climate we treated birds in this manner there would be an outcry. The point must be continually made that if we lose *any* species as a result of our carelessness, rather than factors out of our control such as climatic changes, this is a tragedy for

the generations which follow us. It is the loss of unique habitats which we must all fight against.

The Odonata is divided into two sub-orders, the damselflies (Zygoptera), of which there are seventeen species, and the larger hawker, darter or true dragonflies (Anisoptera), of which there are twenty-seven species. There are several points of distinction between the two. The Zygoptera are much more slender and fly more delicately, the fore and hind wings being very similar. This contrasts with the strong flying of the much more bulky Anisoptera, which in addition have an obvious swelling near the base of the hind wings. A damselfly rests with its wings closed over the abdomen while a hawker rests with its wings spread. A further obvious distinction is that the compound eyes of the hawkers, with the exception of the club tailed dragonfly (*Gomphus vulgatissimus*), are joined over the head, while the two organs are clearly separated in the damselflies.

The whole order is fiercely carnivorous and these hunters feed on flying insects, including unwary smaller members of their own order. There is a great deal of evidence to prove that feeding territories are fiercely protected and that boundary disputes are just as common in these colourful insects as they are in birds.

Breeding is a complex business involving a unique method of

copulation. The female is seized in the region of her thorax by the male's tail appendages, which clasp her; she is then dragged around with the male in the so-called tandem position until they alight on waterside vegetation and sperm transfer is effected. In some species the tandem position is maintained until after the female has made incisions in the stems of water plants, either just above or just below the water level, into

A mating pair of southern aeshna dragonflies. The mate, above, is holding the female by the neck.   *George E. Hyde*

which the egg is placed. Other species break free of the tandem position after copulation and the eggs are dropped into the water as the female skims low over it, her abdomen occasionally touching the surface.

The larvae are totally aquatic and, like their parents, fierce predators. They catch their prey in the mask, a structure formed from the fusion of jaws and a lip-like structure called the labium, which bears strong, sharp, claw-like structures. The mask is kept folded tightly until needed, when it is shot out quickly to secure the prey.

The larvae of the two types vary in their mode of respiration. In the damselflies there are three leaf-like tracheal gills at the tail end of the body which dissolve oxygen from the water and allow it to diffuse into the watertight system of air tubes constituting the tracheal system which ventilates the body; carbon dioxide passes out in the reverse direction. The larger anisopterids have an even more sophisticated method of respiration. There are spine-like structures arranged around the last segment which help to draw water into the anus, inside which are gills connected to the tracheal system. Apart from respiration this mechanism can be used to allow the normally sluggish nymph to move very quickly—nature's own form of jet propulsion.

It is worth while to sample the mud or silt to look for these nymphs which sometimes, depending upon the species, take several years to develop into adults. It is also exciting to patrol the lush vegetation around stretches of water in search of adults.

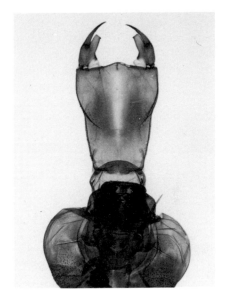

The head and mouth parts of a nymph of the dragonfly, greatly enlarged.
Douglas F. Lawson

Damselflies (Zygoptera)

A few common species likely to be encountered will be described below, but there are so few species that a comparatively short period of study soon brings competence.

Demoiselle (Agrion virgo). The adults of this beautiful species are weak flyers. The males have a blue thorax while that of the female is green; both sexes have greenish-coloured abdomens, but the females can be recognised by the brown tips. The wings of the male are brown, but with a delightful tinge of purple lacking in the duller female, which can be identified by the white tips to her wings. The wing span is about 6 cm (2.4 inches) and the body length about 4.5 cm (1.8 inch). The species is on the wing from late May until October, and the eggs are laid among weeds, those around fairly fast unpolluted streams being preferred. The greenish-brown nymph can reach 3.5 cm (1.4 inch) in length.

White legged damselfly (Platycnemis pennipes). Typified by its white legs, a milky blue colouration and a black line along the top of the abdomen, this species prefers flowing water with plenty of succulent vegetation. The white legs are used in the display by the male as he hovers in front of the female. The body colour only develops some time after hatching, and before it develops the black markings stand out clearly against the light background.

Although the white legged damselfly is rather local in its distribution and is restricted to the South of England, there are some sites where it really is abundant. Conversely there are rivers which would appear to be ideal but along which there are no signs of the insect. Clearly there is a great deal of work yet to be done on the ecology of damselflies in general and on this species in particular.

Large red damselfly (Pyrrhosoma nymphula). In contrast to the distribution of the white legged damselfly that of this species is wide, and areas alongside most slow stretches of rivers and also many canals have large

A damselfly at rest. The wings are folded back over the abdomen, whereas a true dragonfly rests with its wings spread.   *Robert Howe*

populations. They are recognised by the red abdomen—pyrrhosoma means firebody—which has black terminal markings. The black legs are diagnostic, and the females can be separated from the males with just a little practice, females tending to be paler with less distinct black markings, especially those on the head and thorax; the same is true of the yellow stripes which run along the sides.

Common ischnura (Ischnura elegans). The commonest species of damselfly in Britain, *Ischnura elegans* is found abundantly not only alongside canals, ponds and rivers in the countryside but also in the murky waters of town and city as well as in the brackish backwaters and saltmarshes of estuaries. It is on the wing from mid-May until September. The only habitats which seem to cause problems are acidic areas; it is therefore rather scarce in some upland regions of the North and West of Britain.

    Ischnura elegans can be recognised by its black abdomen with a very obvious blue spot on the eighth segment. The thorax of the newly emerged male tends to be apple green but the colour later changes to blue; the thorax of the female varies from apple green to dark green, violet and even orange as well as blue.

    The common blue damselfly (*Enallagma cyathigerum*) is identified by the blue and black patterning along the whole length of the abdomen.

The larger hawker dragonflies

    The sub-order Anisoptera is typified by two species, the brown aeshna (*Aeshna grandis*), which is particularly common in the South-east of Britain, and the common aeshna (*Aeshna juncea*), which is numerous in most aquatic habitats, especially in the North and West.

    The brown aeshna has a wing span of around 10 cm (4 inches) and a body length of around 7.5 cm (3 inches). The distinguishing feature of this species is the yellowish-brown wings which show up very clearly when the insect is in flight. The thorax and the abdomen are dark chocolate brown and there are also patches of yellow on the thorax. A close look at the species at rest will reveal delicate blue areas on the eyes, on the dorsal surface of the thorax and on the abdomen.

    The best time to observe dragonflies at rest is early in the morning. As with all cold-blooded animals, the chill of the night slows down the metabolic rate and body movements are consequently slower. Just after dawn the dragonfly spends time holding its wings into the first shafts of sunlight, and gradually becomes more active and more difficult to observe closely as the day warms up. The sexes can be distinguished, but not easily; the abdomen of the female is thicker than that of the male and there are fewer blue areas on her body.

125

An aeshna dragonfly at rest, its wings spread wide. This fierce predator is one of the most beautiful creatures to be found along the waterways. *Robert Howe*

The common aeshna, also known as the common hawker, is the most widespread of our dragonflies and around the same size as the brown aeshna. The common hawker has proved well able to survive our interference with the environment; it thrives around towns, despite polluted water, and can also survive in rivers running through coniferous plantations. On the wing from July to October, it often flies at dusk. The male has a brown body with yellow on the thorax and the abdomen, which also has pairs of blue spots; the female lacks yellow on the thorax and the spots on the abdomen are green.

Stoneflies (Plecoptera)

Few orders are more aquatic than the stoneflies; their larvae invariably prefer fast-moving water. The biology of stoneflies was discussed in chapter two. The larger species, particularly the genus *Perla*, are carnivorous and feed on worms, crustaceans and the larvae of insects including the smaller stoneflies. They have large eyes, and also rely on

126

long jointed antennae, sensitive hairs and bristles as well as unusual structures called spikelets, which are thought to be organs of smell or perhaps taste. The smaller stoneflies include the genus *Nemoura*, which are vegetarians.

Water bugs (Hemiptera)

The Hemiptera make up a very large order of insects, the majority being terrestrial. The aquatic forms are placed in the sub-order Heteroptera, which are typified by having two different types of wing, the forewings being horny and only partly transparent, the hind wings completely transparent. Bugs can be recognised by their needle-like mouth parts, called the rostrum. Ten families are recognised, of which five, Veliidae, Hydrometridae, Gerridae, Notonectidae and Corixidae, are commonly found in and around streams and rivers.

Water crickets (Veliidae)

The favourite habitat of these little predators, which measure around 0.6 cm (0.25 inch), is the slow-moving backwaters of streams and rivers. They are able to run delicately along the surface of the water, but can also dive in search of insects. The adults are usually but not always wingless, and can be recognised even in the immature stages by an

A water cricket, *Velia*, which runs along the surface of the water in search of its insect prey.
John Clegg

orange ventral surface. The eggs are laid in long strings which are tangled around floating plants. Development depends upon temperature to some extent, but after going through five larval stages adults eventually emerge; as many as three generations occur each day.

Water measurers (Hydrometridae)

Moving ponderously along the surface, the two species of water gnat are so thin that it is difficult to work out where the body organs are situated. *Hydrometra stagnorum* is common in shallow water lapping the stems of aquatic vegetation. The wingless body is covered with hairs which act as a water-proofing, while the three pairs of legs are spread so wide that *Hydrometra* never falls through the water film; they do seem to operate like calipers, measuring the water. The water measurers wait for water insects coming up for air and then plunge their rostrum into their tissues. The peak of the breeding season is early summer, and two generations are produced each year.

Pond skaters (Gerridae)

There is only one family of these fascinating animals in Europe and there are ten species, one of the most common being *Gerris najas*. The female is invariably larger than her mate and is 1.7 cm (0.66 inch) long, the male, who is 1.4 cm (0.55 inch), often riding around on her back. The most common of the British pond skaters, also found in streams and slow-moving rivers, is *Gerris lacustris*, a species seldom reaching 1 cm (0.39 inch). Pond skaters are typified by their long legs which are spread as they move delicately over the water surface. Any insect tumbling from the vegetation overhanging the river is quickly stabbed by the sharp beak, slowed down by an injection of toxin and sucked dry.

Water boatmen (Notonectidae)

Four species occur in Britain, the family being typified by the fact that they swim upside down and draw air via two spiracles into the tracheal system along a network of tubes formed from long abdominal hairs. It is when air fills these canals that the centre of gravity of the animal is altered and it turns upside down. The movement of *Notonecta* is effected by the rhythmic rowing action of long hairy hind legs. Although normally associated with still water, water boatmen also occur in the sheltered backwaters of streams and rivers, where they feed on fish eggs and also quite large aquatic insects. *Notonecta glauca* can be up to 1.6 cm (0.6 inch) long and is capable of inflicting a painful bite on an unwary human hand. The species can fly well and during the autumn females can often be seen searching for suitable water plants in which to lay the eggs. The greenish white larvae look very like wingless adults and are sexually mature after five moults.

Lesser waterboatmen (Corixidae)

Typified by their swarming behaviour, the Corixidae, of which there are over thirty species, are less dense than water; if they wish to remain below the surface they are obliged to hang on to water weeds by means of their very powerful claws. Despite their confusing vernacular name they are around the same size as the water boatman but are distinguished from it by their ability to swim the right way up. They do, however, take smaller prey as well as a considerable amount of detritus. They use their hind legs for swimming; the mature adults possess wings and during mating, which takes place mainly in the spring, the males of several species can produce a strident cricket-like chirping. They are also surprisingly resistant to low temperatures and spend the winter months as adults.

Lacewings (Neuroptera)

The best-known British species is the giant lacewing (*Osmylus fulvicephalus*), which has a wing span of up to 5 cm (2 inches). It is easily recognised by its orange head and black body, and the magnificent

A lacewing at rest on the stem of a waterside plant, its wings folded over the body like a sloping roof. *John Clegg*

iridescence on the net-like wings which are blotched with brown. When lacewings are at rest the wings are held over the body like a sloping roof. The species can be common in the vegetation along riversides, especially from April to June. The females lay their eggs on the leaves of waterside plants, the larvae hunting their food, mainly insect larvae, among the damp riverside moss, occasionally venturing into the water. The long jaws projecting in front of the head are formidable weapons.

Another interesting species is the 'sponge-fly' *Sisyra*, the larvae of which live on the body surface of freshwater sponges, often boring into the body of the animal. Their elongated jaws can be formed into a temporary tube through which body fluids can be sucked.

Beetles (Coleoptera)

Five families of beetle are represented in fresh water, three of them frequently being seen in and around rivers. There is ample evidence to suggest that their invasion of the aquatic habitat has been recent, at least in evolutionary terms.

More than 100 species of beetles of the family Dytiscidae are found in Britain, by far the most spectacular being the predatory *Dytiscus marginalis*. Adults can be as long as 3.5 cm (1.4 inch) and the larva is often as much as twice this length. The jaws of both larvae and adults are strong enough to overcome tadpoles and small fish as well as invertebrates; freshwater biologists should be very careful how they handle them. *Dytiscus* flies strongly, especially at night, and often lands on wet roads in mistake for a river or pond. The body margin is etched with

A *Dytiscus* beetle, whose strong jaws enable it to attack tadpoles and small fish as well as invertebrates.
Alan W. Heath

ond skater (*Gerris* sp.)   *John Clegg*   A damselfly.

ewly emerged southern hawker (*Aeshna cyanea*).   *B. Ogden*

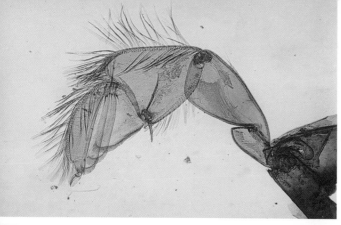

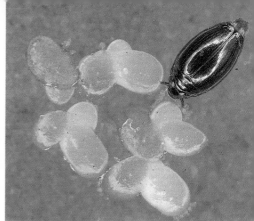

A whirligig beetle (*Gyrinus natator*), above, and a greatly enlarged view of its rear leg, above left, showing how well it is adapted to swimming. At left is the larva of an alderfly (*Sialis lutaria*) and below is the adult alderfly crawling among the waterside vegetation.

All by John Clegg

yellow, and the male is recognised by a sucker on the foreleg which he uses to grip the female during pairing, while females can be recognised by the corrugated appearance of the wing cases. After a period in water the larva crawls back on to land to pupate, a clear indication of its terrestrial origins. The adult beetles, although very efficient divers, draw air into spiracles sited at the rear of the body. The waste carbon dioxide escapes gradually and is collected in a bubble between the wing cases (called elytra) and the abdomen, this bubble being used to regulate the buoyancy of the body.

The whirligig beetles (Gyrinidae) are often the first animals to be noticed along the waterside because of their habit of swimming in circles at fantastic speed. Try to catch one, however, and they dive quickly. Their compound eyes show an interesting adaptation to life on the surface, being divided into two halves by a furrow—a perfect example of a bifocal lens.

The nineteen species of dark brown or black Dryopoidea beetles are particularly interesting to the river-based naturalist since they are adapted to life in fast-moving, well-oxygenated water and feed upon the algae and mosses encrusting the stones. The hairy bodies enable the beetle to trap an air bubble which functions like a 'lung' into which oxygen can diffuse and carbon dioxide escape. The animal is therefore totally aquatic and does not need to come to the surface to breathe oxygen direct from the atmosphere. This also explains why the Dryopoidea can only live in richly oxygenated water and is a truly river-based family.

The larva of the great silver beetle, a member of one of the five families of beetle which have adapted to life in fresh water.   *John Clegg*

Alderflies (Megaloptera)

Only two species of alderfly are found in Britain, *Sialis lutaria* and *Sialis fuligenosa*. Adult alderflies are typified by four wings but they do not fly well, preferring to crawl among the leaves of waterside vegetation. The larva must leave the water to pupate, but it can survive its early

Left: An alderfly, *Sialis*, clinging to the stem of a waterside plant. Not a strong flier, the alderfly prefers to crawl among the stems and leaves of waterside vegetation. **Right:** The egg-mass of alderfly.   *John Clegg*

developmental period at great depths in the bottom mud and if necessary in polluted areas often very deficient in oxygen. Adult alderflies measure about 1 cm (0.4 inch), but the larvae are often twice this size.

Caddisflies (Trichoptera)

Caddisflies are superficially rather like moths, but there are several easily detectable differences. The two pairs of wings are hairy and membranous, and when at rest the wings are held in a roof. The name Trichoptera means hairy wings; moths, on the other hand, have scaly wings. There are around 190 British species of Trichoptera, divided into two groups. Some have so-called compodeid larvae, with the head and body axis held in a straight line; others have cruciform types, in which the head is carried at right angles to the body axis. The cruciform type of larva always lives within a protective case made from a web of silk in which pebbles or rootlets are embedded, these cases ensuring that caddisflies are among the first aquatic insects to be encountered and studied by beginners.

Identification of adult caddisflies is very difficult, but some progress was made by M. E. Mosely in his book published in 1949 (see bibliography). The largest and one of the commonest British species is *Phryganea grandis*, which has a wing span of around 5 cm (2 inches); the wings are brownish, splashed with lighter blotches, and the antennae are long and flexible. The tiny greenish eggs are laid in batches of up to 700 embedded in jelly, which looks like a smoke ring. Depending upon temperature, the larvae hatch in about ten days and immediately set about building a case, using pieces of water plant arranged spirally to form rather a pretty pattern. Caddisflies which live mainly in still waters, like *Phryganea*, make their cases of the lightest possible material so that movement is easier. In some species, *Agapetus fuscipes* for example, life in moving water necessitates a heavy case constructed of pebbles and grains of sand which will prevent the animal from being flushed downstream. There are some caddisfly larvae which live in swiftly flowing streams, one such species being *Hydropsyche angustipennis*; this does not build a case at all but spins a net of silk between stones and uses this to catch insect larvae and other food. The majority of the caddisfly larvae do make cases and are vegetarian.

Butterflies and moths (Lepidoptera)

There are no aquatic forms of butterfly and only the china mark moths undergo part of their life cycle in water. Like the caddisflies, the larvae of the china mark moth build cases; the two can be easily distinguished because the legs of the china mark moths are so much shorter. The name derives from the similarity between potters' trade marks and the wing patterns of the adults.

More common in still waters, china mark moths are found in the backwaters of rivers and streams, especially where there is an abundance of floating leaves of water lilies and pond weeds such as *Potamogeton*. After the larvae have hatched they cut pieces out of the underside of leaves and sandwich themselves between the piece and the leaf, the joint being 'stitched' with silk. A common species is the brown china mark moth (*Nymphula mympheata*), whose larva is in its early stages able to absorb oxygen all over its body surface direct from the water. Later, after a number of moults, air is trapped inside the silky case and the developing tracheal system is fed by this trapped air.

Cataclysta lemnata feeds on and makes its case out of duckweed. The brown female can be easily distinguished from the basically white male. The adults measure around 1.1 cm (0.43 inch) and the larvae are just a fraction larger. Adults fly from June to August, a time when the brown china mark moths are also on the wing. The latter species can reach 1.7 cm (0.7 inch) as an adult and the larvae are around 2.0 cm (0.8 inch). In one species of china mark moth, *Acentria nivea*, two forms of female occur, one without wings which spends her time under water, only

The larval cases of china mark moth caterpillars on a waterlily leaf. The larvae cut pieces out of the leaf and sandwich themselves between the cut piece and the leaf, "stitching" the joint with silk.

John Clegg

pushing her abdomen through the surface film to be fertilised by a passing male; the other female form has normal wings.

Flies (Diptera)

The majority of aquatic insect larvae belong to the *Diptera* order; their study is difficult and many new British species are awaiting discovery. Some idea of the vast populations can be had by looking at the midges (Chironomidae family), of which there are over 400 species in Britain alone. The larvae often construct cases which are secured to stones or water plants, enabling the insect to survive in fast-moving water. They feed mainly on plant material which is usually dead and decaying, but a few are carnivorous. They themselves are fed upon by fish and therefore occupy an important position in the centre of the food chain.

The adult life is very short and has the sole object of reproducing the species. They do not suck blood, and although the swarms can be a nuisance to the riverside stroller they do not bite. In contrast the mosquitoes and gnats of the Culicidae family can suck blood, but it is only the females of a few species which do this, probably because they require blood for their eggs to mature. The males, which have a shorter life, feed on nectar and drink frequently.

The Dixidae and Chaoboridae are related families which do not suck blood; one of the commonest species is *Chaoborus crystallinus*, the phantom midge. The aquatic larvae, which are around 1.2 cm (0.5 inch) long, are almost transparent and difficult to see, thus accounting for their vernacular names of phantom midge and glass larva. They are rendered even more difficult to see by their habit of remaining motionless, held in position by a pair of air-filled bladders at either end of body. The carnivorous larvae called blood worms are eaten by fish, as are members of the Chironomidae family—the true midges—which have high levels of haemoglobin in their blood, thus enabling them to live in polluted rivers. The Simuliidae or blackflies have larvae which filter their food from fast-running water and adults which can inflict a painful bite—it is the blackflies which can cause cattle and horses grazing in water meadows to panic.

The soldier flies of the Stratiomyidae family are not only harmless but beautifully coloured, the abdomen being brightly ringed with yellow on black. Another family with a superficial resemblance to bees are the hoverflies of the Syrphidae family, of which there are more than a thousand species. Only one genus, however, is aquatic and this is *Eristalis* (tubifers). The larva is recognised by its long breathing tube which can be up to 10 cm (4 inches) long, allowing the animal to live in muddy water and still breathe atmospheric air; this tube earns the larva the vernacular name of 'rat-tailed maggot'.

There is no space in a book of this nature to describe the flies in detail but some brief mention must be made of the Craneflies or daddy-long-legs, which are grouped into two very similar families, the Tipulidae and Limnobiidae. An expert is needed to separate the two by reference to the veining on the wings and the detailed construction of the mouth parts. The largest species is *Acutipula maxima*, which has a wing span of around 6.5 cm (2.55 inches). Most larvae, known as leather-jackets, are found in damp soil, but they are also able to survive in the mud at the bottom of the stream.

Ants, bees and wasps (Hymenoptera)

Very few of the Hymenoptera are able to cope with aquatic conditions, but a few wasps attack other invertebrates, especially water beetles. In the case of one wasp, *Mestocharis bimacularis*, the eggs are laid on the eggs of water beetles; it is probably wrong to refer to this wasp as a parasite because the host is always killed, so it is usually referred to as a parasitoid. *Mestocharis bimacularis* as an adult is not aquatic and must wait for dry spells before it can find a suitable host on which to lay its eggs, but another wasp, *Caraphractus cinctus*, uses its wings to swim under the surface of the water in search of the eggs of water beetles, dragonflies and alderflies.

137

Agriotypus armatus lays its eggs in caddisfly larvae; when they hatch the young wasps feed on the caddisfly but avoid eating its main organs, only destroying it completely in the pupal stage.

Spiders and mites (Arachnida)

Only one species of spider, *Argyroneta aquatica*, lives permanently in water. It measures up to 1.6 cm (0.63 inch) in length and its brownish body is usually made to look like polished silver by a bubble of air coating the abdomen. The species makes a bell of silk which it fills with air, using this as its underwater home. The food, which consists of invertebrates, is carried back to the bell before being eaten. The water spider moults several times during its life; because it is particularly vulnerable to predators when moulting it builds specially strengthened moulting shelters. The species is found in ditches, slow-moving rivers and the pools of their upland catchment areas.

Much more common are the predatory water-mites; those which are found in fast streams and rivers are usually provided with tough claws

Water-mite.   *Carole Pugh*

and stiff bristles which enable them to cling tightly to stones and vegetation. The legs are often hairy and can function like broad paddles when swift movement is required. Water mites have evolved from terrestrial forms and have sharp mandibles which can pierce the bodies of invertebrates to suck out the fluids, leaving behind a hollow husk. The two spiracles through which they breathe are situated near the mouth parts and are closed by a thin membrane through which oxygen enters and carbon dioxide is exhaled; thus water mites have no need to journey to the water surface to breathe.

There are in excess of 300 species in Britain, most of them dull white or bright red in colour. The various species are difficult to identify, identification not being helped by the fact that most measure less than 0.3 cm (0.12 inch). They do not have a definite head and look rather like a tiddly-wink gyrating through the water. Although many of the water mite larvae are parasites, especially on water beetles and also on other invertebrates, the adults are free living and common in all types of fresh water.

CHAPTER EIGHT

Fish of the River

THE streamlined body of a fish is well known even to non-naturalists but the function of the various organs, especially the fins, is seldom properly understood.

The main locomotory organ is the powerfully muscular tail, which makes up the bulk of the posterior portion of the body. The tail is employed like a sculling oar to drive the fish through the water, the power being produced by longitudinal muscle fibres which first contract and then relax. The muscle blocks are on opposite sides of the vertebral column, and this produces S-shaped waves which pass along the tail, generating a forward but rotating movement which is stabilised by unpaired fins such as the ventral, anal and dorsal. The paired organs, the pelvic and pectoral fins, which are equivalent to our arms and legs, are used to steer the fish and often also as brakes. Many freshwater fish also possess an organ called the swim bladder which allows the animal to control its position in the water without sinking or rising to the surface.

The swim bladder

Fish are obviously heavier than the water in which they live and therefore tend to sink. Species without swim bladders hold the pectoral fins at an angle so that they function as lifting foils. This lifting action is bound to create a significant drag, which means that the fish has to keep moving to prevent itself from sinking and cannot therefore hover or swim backwards. While this does not much matter in species living in the sea or in large freshwater lakes, fish inhabiting the confined parameters of ponds and rivers require more control over buoyancy, and the swim bladder, providing what is termed static lift, is the ideal organ for freshwater fish. The fish's body is not greatly heavier than the water and can achieve neutral buoyancy by storing light gases in the swim bladder. In marine fish which possess these valuable organs it has been estimated that around five per cent of the body volume is occupied by the swim bladders, but in many freshwater species this figure may be between seven and eight per cent. Many fish also possess large deposits of oils which are less dense than water and also give a degree of static lift.

It seems fairly certain that the swim bladder originated as a blind-ending pouch from the foregut, and in fish such as the eels the structure is still linked to the gut. Zoologists are convinced that its original function

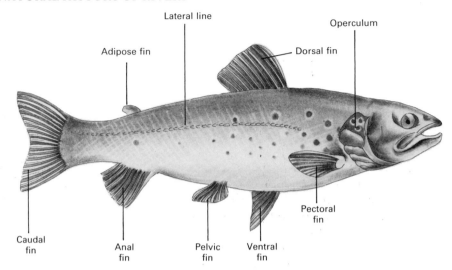

Lateral line

Operculum

Adipose fin

Dorsal fin

Caudal fin

Anal fin

Pelvic fin

Ventral fin

Pectoral fin

was as an auxiliary breathing organ, and this may well be one reason why eels can survive for long periods out of water. In most bony fish, however, the bladder is sealed off early in the development of the young fish and is either full of gas from the outset or is able to absorb gas directly from the cells which line its wall. It has been shown by the use of radioactive tracers that the oxygen in the swim bladder derives from that absorbed from the water through the gills and carried in the blood stream and is not generated by any chemical activity on the part of the cells themselves. There is plenty of evidence that the pressure in the swim bladder affects the co-ordination of the fins, enabling the fish to keep at the optimum depth in the water.

The lateral line system

If it is to respond to variations in current strength and direction a fish must have a sensitive organ to detect such changes. This is the function of the lateral line system, which consists of a fine network of fluid-filled canals just under the skin with a number of pores leading to the exterior. The system has two main and usually visible branches, one on each side of the body, running from the front of the trunk almost to the end of the tail. At the head end the system 'opens out' into an intermingling network covering the head and snout.

In the lateral line system there are sensitive structures called neuromasts, each made up of a number of cells set on a cushion-like structure carried on the inner wall of the canal. Each cell has a very sensitive tip which connects with a nerve fibre leading via the vagus nerve to the brain. Fish can therefore quickly detect vibrations in the water, measure depth and appreciate the presence of prey or predators; there is evidence suggesting that low-frequency vibrations can also be detected.

Reflections from other fish may well be important in keeping shoals of fish together and preventing one individual from colliding with another. There is also some feedback as a result of the fish's own movement which serves to co-ordinate its swimming.

Breathing
Bony fish, and all freshwater fish are of this group, obtain oxygen directly from the water by means of the gills, carbon dioxide passing out in the reverse direction. The gills are usually covered by a flap called the operculum, beneath which there are five pairs of gill slits leading to four pairs of gills which penetrate directly into the pharynx. Each gill is supported by an arch from which hang a number of gill filaments extremely rich in blood, greatly increasing the surface area over which

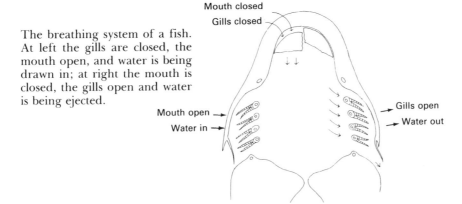

Mouth closed
Gills closed

The breathing system of a fish. At left the gills are closed, the mouth open, and water is being drawn in; at right the mouth is closed, the gills open and water is being ejected.

Mouth open →
Water in →

Gills open →
Water out →

oxygen and carbon dioxide can diffuse into and out of the blood. To ensure a constant supply of oxygen-rich water over the gills the fish can alter the pressure inside the mouth, enabling it to suck in water and then pump it out over the gills. The fish opens its mouth at the same time as it closes the gill slits; the floor of the mouth is then pulled down by powerful muscles, the increasing volume reducing the pressure in the mouth and water therefore enters. The mouth is then closed, the gill slits opened and water forced out over them by raising the floor of the mouth, thereby increasing the pressure.

Beneath the operculum are important structures known as gill rakers serving to filter out rough particles which might otherwise become lodged in and damage the delicate gills. Unlike mammals, which have a separate circulation to the lungs, the fish has only a single blood circulation and is unable to hold its body temperature constant, a condition known as poikilothermic. Mammals and birds which can control their body temperature are termed homosothermic. This inability to control body temperature is, however, no disadvantage to fish since the temperature deep in the water varies very little over the year; as we saw in chapter one, ice forming on top of the water in winter provides insulation against extremely low temperatures and fish seldom have to live in conditions below 4°C.

The skin

Fish are so streamlined that they need little energy to move, and this is further helped by the provision of a layer of slime called mucus produced by glands in the skin. In some species the layer of mucus is thick enough to prevent damage to the delicate skin, while in others additional protection is given by the scales.

The scale pattern is often unique to the species and skilled scientists are able to separate similar species by counting the scales. They are counted downwards and forwards from the dorsal fin to the lateral line and then from the lateral line to the start of the pelvic fin, the count being used to produce a ratio enabling a species to be recognised. Another interesting aspect is that the age of a fish can often be calculated by reference to the scales, which have annual rings rather like those used to calculate the age of a tree. The growth increments are rather more difficult to assess than in the case of trees, and much care and skill is needed if real accuracy is to be achieved.

Fish and water

All water contains some salt in solution, and seawater obviously contains high levels. The body fluids of fish are also salty and tend to fall between the two extremes of salinity. The process of osmosis is defined as the movement of water from a weak to a strong solution through a semi-permeable membrane; the gills act as a semi-permeable membrane and because seawater is more concentrated than the body fluids a marine fish loses water and tends to dehydrate, a problem the fish overcomes by drinking seawater and excreting the unwanted salt through glands in the gills. In freshwater the fish has the opposite problem of continuously absorbing water, which it solves by having large and efficient kidneys.

The eye of a fish

Vision is usually the most important sense in fish; the eyes are extremely well developed and the majority of freshwater species have excellent colour vision. Although species such as catfish, salmon and eels have a wonderful sense of smell, most rely heavily on sight feeding.

We should not assume, however, that the fish's vision is identical to our own. Water is a poor transmitter of light, and salt and fresh water have different optical qualities. Oceans are blue like the Mediterranean, blue-green like the Baltic or grey like the North Sea, while lakes and rivers tend to be greenish-yellow. Only light with a very short wavelength can penetrate to any great depth in seawater and the colour sensitivity of

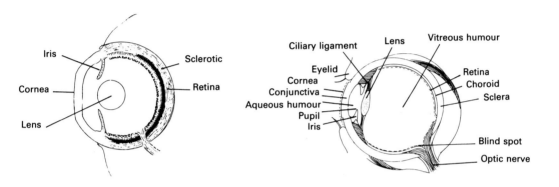

The fish's eye, left, compared with the eye of a mammal.   *Carole Pugh*

marine fish is shifted towards the blue end of the spectrum. Freshwater species are more sensitive at the red end of the spectrum, a shift of sensitivity particularly obvious in shallow-water species such as the perch (*Perca fluviatilis*). This may well explain why many species of fish found in rivers and streams have red fins which are often used in display.

In all fish the cornea is flatter, while in land-based vertebrates, including man, this structure is curved. The refractive index of the cornea is almost the same as water; this means that it plays no part in focusing light, this job being done by a large spherical lens of very short focal length. The cornea does, however, protect the eye from silt and swirling water. Because of the shape of the lens fish are very short sighted, but the fish can accommodate for distant vision by pulling and pushing the lens in a manner very like the focusing mechanism of a camera.

Mammals are able to adjust to sudden changes in light intensity by means of the eyelids and also by the diaphragm-like structure of the iris. The fish has none of these and must adjust slowly as dawn gives way to bright sunshine. There is no doubt that when lights are switched on suddenly aquarium fishes feel some distress, as do fish pulled out of the depths of a pool by an angler. Most fish are able to adapt to changes in light intensity by shifting pigments around the sensitive areas to filter out light. The problem posed by sudden changes in light intensity might well explain why fish remain in a favourite depth of water during the day and then rise to feed during twilight. Vision in low intensity light cannot be easy but fish have solved the problem by the evolution of a tapetum, a reflecting layer which is found in the retina. The tapeta consist of iridescent cells which reflect light and function like mirrors to increase the light intensity.

Many species have iridescent areas on their scales which mirror the background and make them difficult targets for predators.

The classification of British freshwater fish

Table five shows a classification of the British freshwater fish, but some are confined to ponds or lakes and are not found in rivers. It will be noticed that the lampreys belonging to the family Petromyzanidae are not included in the table; this is because the lampreys are not grouped with the fish since their supportive tissue is made almost entirely of cartilage, they do not possess scales and they do not have jaws, having

Table 5. Simplified Table of the Freshwater Fish of Britain

| | Species | |
Family	English Name	Scientific Name
Acipenseridae	sturgeon	*Acipenser sturio*
Clupeidae	allis shad	*Alosa alosa*
	twaite shad	*Alosa fallax*
Salmonidae	salmon	*Salmo salar*
	sea/brown trout	*Salmo trutta*
	rainbow trout	*Salmo gairdneri*
	brook char	*Salvelinus fontinalis*
	char	*Salvelinus alpinus*
Coregonidae	whitefish	*Coregonus laveretus*
	vendace	*Coregonus albula*
	houting	*Coregonus oxyrinchus*

Thymallidae	grayling	*Thymallus thymallus*
Osmeridae	smelt	*Osmerus eperlanus*
Esocidae	pike	*Esox lucius*
Cyprinidae	carp	*Cyprinus carpio*
	crucian carp	*Carassius carassius*
	goldfish	*Carassius auratus*
	tench	*Tinca tinca*
	gudgeon	*Gobio gobio*
	barbel	*Barbus barbus*
	bream	*Abramis brama*
	silver bream	*Blicca bjoerkna*
	bleak	*Alburnus alburnus*
	minnow	*Phoxinus phoxinus*
	bitterling	*Rhodeus sericeus*
	rudd	*Scardinius erythrophthalmus*
	roach	*Rutilus rutilus*
	chub	*Leuciscus cephalus*
	orfe	*Leuciscus idus*
	dace	*Leuciscus leuciscus*
Cobitidae	stone loach	*Noemacheilus barbatulus*
	spined loach	*Cobitis taenia*
Gasterosteidae	three spined stickleback	*Gasterosteus aculeatus*
	ten spined stickleback	*Pungitius pungitius*
Siluridae	wels	*Siluris glanis*
Anguillidae	eel	*Anguilla anguilla*
Gadidae	burbot	*Lota lota*
Serranidae	sea bass	*Dicentrarchus labrax*
Centrarchidae	Large mouthed bass	*Micropterus salmoides*
	pumpkinseed	*Lepomis gibbosus*
	rock bass	*Ambloplites rupestris*
Percidae	perch	*Perca fluviatilis*
	ruffe	*Gymnocephalus cernua*
	zander	*Stizostedion lucioperca*
Gobiidae	common goby	*Pomatoschistus microps*
Cottidae	bullhead	*Cottus gobio*
Mugilidae	thick lipped mullet	*Crenimugil labrosus*
	thin lipped mullet	*Chelon ramada*
	golden mullet	*Chelon auratus*
Pleuronectidae	flounder	*Platichthys flesus*

instead a sucking disc by which they secure themselves to fish on which they live as parasites. There are three British species, of which two are anadromous, which means that like the salmon they breed in fresh water and mature at sea. For this reason the lampreys must be considered in any book on the natural history of rivers.

Lampreys

River lamprey or lampern *(Lampetra fluviatilis)*

At one time this species was an important food fish; numbers seem to have decreased largely as a result of man's activities. Pollution has obviously taken its toll in recent years, but obstructions such as weirs, dams and navigation locks have probably been an even greater problem to the lamprey. Although rather scarce in northern Scotland, it is still widely distributed in British rivers; while it does spend some time at sea, the lamprey does not seem to venture too far from the shore. The lampern seems to find most clean rivers, streams and the occasional lake to its liking; it prefers those with a stony or sandy bed for its spawning site, which is visited usually in autumn though a few do breed in spring.

A strange event in the life of a maturing female is the development of an anal fin, which might enable her to position her eggs more efficiently. The larvae remain in the mud for as long as six years before reaching a length of around 1.3 cm (0.5 inch) and moving to the sea, where they spend up to two years. They can grow to over 50 cm (19.7 inches). At this stage the lamprey resembles an eel, but can readily be distinguished by its lack of an operculum and by the presence of seven small circular openings on either side of the head. The sucker-like mouth and the absence of paired fins are also important points of distinction.

Brook lamprey *(Lampetra pluneri)*

Although its distribution is similar to that of the lampern, this species is probably the most common lamprey in Britain and is overlooked because of its superficial resemblance to the eel. The brook lamprey seldom exceeds 25 cm (almost 10 inches) and is non-migratory; as its name implies it is found more often in streams than in large deep rivers.

The larvae feed on small aquatic organisms and detritus on the stream bed. It is only after five or six years in a larval state that the brook lamprey reaches adulthood; despite the presence of a suction disc the teeth are poorly developed, and it is unlikely that the adults feed at all. Spawning takes place between April and June, and after the eggs have been fertilised the adults die, their job in ensuring the survival of the species done.

Sea lamprey *(Petromyson marinus)*

Despite its name, the sea lamprey spends most of its life in fresh water, buried deep in the silt and mud of the lowland reaches of a river. It finds ample food among the numerous invertebrates which share this habitat and only moves upstream into the fast, clear streams to breed. The mature adults, however, may not go directly to the spawning beds but spend up to three years at sea.

The largest of the sea lampreys, mature females, which are usually larger than the males, can reach a length of 90 cm (35.5 inches). The adult is a true parasite complete with powerful suction disc, a rough rasping tongue and a supply of anti-coagulant which keeps the blood of its prey flowing.

True fishes

Some twenty families are represented in Britain's fresh waters, but some of these are only occasional visitors. Included here is the sturgeon (*Acipenser sturio*), belonging to the Acipenseridae, a primitive family having bony plates along the body instead of scales. So few individuals enter Britain's waters that most river watchers are never likely to see one nor will there ever be a caviar industry in Britain.

The Clupeidae or shad family is represented in Britain by two anadromous species, the allis shad (*Alosa alosa*) and the twaite shad (*Alosa fallax*). The shads are estuarine fish which are deep chested and fleshy, sometimes reaching 60 cm (24 inches) and weighing up to 2.7 kg (6 lb). They spawn high up fast-moving rivers and have proved particularly susceptible to both pollution and overfishing. The herring-like flesh was at one time much sought after, and the west coast of Britain once had large commercial shad fisheries; those who tend to be complacent about the future of salmon in Britain would do well to remember the shad.

Salmonidae

This economically important family is represented by the salmon, brook and common char, and the trout. All these species have been described in previous chapters, as have the migratory sea trout and the resident brown trout. This leaves the introduced rainbow trout (*Salmo gairdneri*) which is so popular with fish farmers. The family is typified by the presence of an adipose fin situated on the dorsal surface close to the tail and also by powerful jaws, this fish sharing the strong predatory tendencies of the salmon.

The Coregonidae family is represented in Britain by three species: the whitefish (*Coregonus laveretus*), the vendace (*Coregonus albula*) and the houting (*Coregonus oxyrinchus*), but they are very uncommon and venture out of the lakes in which they live into cold streams where they spawn only for this purpose. Whitefish are related to the salmon and also have an adipose fin on the dorsal surface.

The Thymallidae family has only one British representative, the grayling, a species which was described in chapter two. The Osmeridae family also has only one British species, the smelt (*Osmerus eperlanus*), which is now confined to coastal waters and estuaries. At one time there were some smelt in isolated lakes, presumably left after the ice ages, but these are now extinct in Britain though not in other parts of Europe.

The next family to be described, the Esocidae, is also represented by a single species, but this fox of the river and lake is never likely to be overlooked.

Pike (*Esox lucius*)

Pike are widespread throughout mainland Britain and also in Ireland, where they were introduced. The favoured habitat is lakes or slow-moving rivers, although they are found in faster streams providing

Pike.   *Carole Pugh*

there is a fringe of vegetation in which they can hide. It is difficult to establish the favourite habitat of the pike because of its popularity with anglers, both as a sporting and as an edible species, which has resulted in waters being artificially stocked with fish. In Britain a good specimen might reach 130 cm (51 inches) in length and weigh up to 24 kg (53 lb). The female pike is always considerably larger than the male, and the larger specimens are rather tough to eat, but a small 'jack' pike baked in butter is one of the gastronomic delights to grace the angler's table.

Pike can live for more than twenty years but are usually sexually mature at three and often as early as two years. Early spring is the peak period for spawning, when the female lays her sticky eggs on fringing vegetation. Depending upon temperature, the young pike hatch out between a week and a fortnight following egg laying. Spawning and

Brown trout have suffered greatly from pollution, disturbance and overfishing, but where the rivers are kept in good condition they give the angler good sport. Between October and February the fish move on to gravel beds to spawn, and the infant trout, right, hatch after four to six weeks. A young brown trout such as that seen below can, if living in rich waters, grow eventually to a length of a metre or more. *John Clegg*

A perch (*Perca fluviatilis*), found in slower,
more weedy stretches of river.   *John Clegg*

A chub (*Leuciscus cephalus*).
John Clegg

The rudd (*Scardinius erythrophthalmus*) in its natural habitat of weed-choked river.   *Michael Edwards*

feeding take place during daylight, since pike have excellent eyesight. The young feed on invertebrates but grow rapidly, and soon their powerful jaws are snapping up fish. Since it is such a fierce predator the number of pike in any aquatic habitat must be limited by the available food supply. Large pike will tackle mammals and birds as well as fish; I once saw a full-grown rat snapped up by a pike, and young waterfowl, including cygnets, are in continual danger.

Cyprinidae

The carp family is well represented in British waters and several of the sixteen British species have already been described, including the barbel (*Barbus barbus*), bream (*Abramis brama*), minnow (*Phoxinus phoxinus*) and chub (*Leuciscus cephalus*). Five of our sixteen species have been introduced, and all are typified by the absence of scales on the head, although the body is well scaled. They all have a single dorsal fin and none possess teeth, although many have sharp, tough lips which carry out the same function.

They are a difficult family to identify with precision since there is a great deal of hybridisation. They can usually be positively identified by reference to the pharyngeal bones.

Carp

Most authorities recognise three varieties of the common carp (*Cyprinus carpio*) in ponds, canals and slow-moving rivers of Britain. These are the scaled, leather and mirror carp, but the true ancestor of all three has probably been lost after centuries of cross-breeding. Carp are easy to keep in fish ponds, are good to eat if cooked carefully, and survive well in oxygen-deficient waters; they are omnivorous feeders and this gives them the additional advantage to the fish farmer that they can easily be fattened on scraps. All three species were introduced into Britain, probably in the middle ages.

Until recently it was thought that the crucian carp (*Carassius carassius*) was also an introduction, but an examination of material found during archaeological investigation of Roman London revealed bones identified as those from a crucian carp, revealing that if it was introduced it must have been in Roman times or earlier. Crucian carp are often kept in waters with the common carp, and the fact that the species are able to hybridise can cause confusion. Crucian carp grow more slowly than other species and they are therefore not popular with fish farmers. The deep solid body can weigh up to 1.8 kg (4 lb) and reach a length of 50 cm (20 inches). The ground colour is olive-green, with a brownish tinge on the dorsal surface and a yellowish tint on the belly. The fins are basically grey but the pelvic, pectoral and anal fins are shaded with red.

The goldfish (*Carassius auratus*) was introduced from eastern Europe by aquarists, and a few have been released and now live wild in rivers. It will eat aquatic plants, but its main diet consists of invertebrates.

Tench (Tinca tinca)

The tench (*Tinca tinca*) is a native species, particularly common in lowland England. It spends most of its time on the bottom mud and is only found in slow-moving rivers, preferring ponds and canals. The dorsal surface is almost black, and the flanks are dark grey, the ventral surface a delicate orange. Tench can reach a length of 72 cm (28 inches) and weigh as much as 8 kg (17 lb 8 oz), but most specimens are less than half this weight. Male tench can be distinguished by their pelvic fins, which are much longer than those of the females.

Gudgeon (Gobio gobio)

Gudgeon thrive in swiftly flowing streams, especially those with bottoms of sand and gravel. Although very common in England and Wales, it is absent from much of Scotland and the West of Ireland. The

Gudgeon.

Carole Pugh

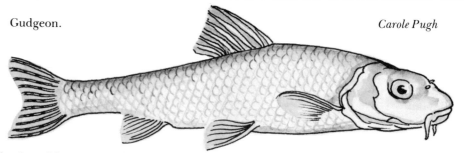

body seldom exceeds 15 cm (6 inches), but specimens of 20 cm (8 inches) do occur, the females tending to be larger than the males. The dorsal surface is greenish-brown, the flanks are yellow marked with eight black blotches, and the ventral surface is silver. The fins, especially the dorsal, anal and caudal, are heavily spotted.

Gudgeon spawn during May or June, the yellowish eggs hatching in two or three weeks, depending upon temperature. Sexual maturity is reached in two or three years and the life span can be as long as seven years. The mature male can be identified by a number of white tubercles on his head. Gudgeon, which are often found in shoals, have a long snout and a pronounced barbel at the corners of the mouth.

At one time gudgeon were eaten, but the species is now of very minor importance as a sporting or gastronomic fish. Gudgeon eat invertebrates and are themselves the prey of larger fish, especially pike, and so are an intermediate but important link in the food chain.

White bream (Blicca bjoerkna)

The bream (*Abramis brama*) has already been described in chapter three, but the white or silver bream (*Blicca bjoerkna*) is also native to the midland counties of Britain, living well in slow-moving rivers, especially those with a rich tapestry of fringing vegetation. It is very much smaller than the common bream, seldom reaching more than 30 cm (12 inches) or weighing more than 450 grams (1 lb). There is also a difference in scales, those of the silver bream being larger. Anglers do not like the silver bream in their swim and do their best to remove it to avoid competition with the common bream, a very popular fighting fish.

Bleak (Alburnus alburnus)

The bleak is another indigenous species found in the South and East of the country. An attractive alert species, the bleak does not exceed 20 cm (8inches). The dorsal surface is blue-grey, but the flanks and belly are a flashing silver. Separated from the somewhat similar dace by its much longer anal fin, the bleak is not popular with anglers, except as a bait for pike. Bleak hybridise with the dace (*Leuciscus leucisus*) as well as with the roach (*Rutilus rutilus*) and the chub (*Leuciscus cephalus*), which can cause problems of identification.

The bitterling (*Rhodeus sericeus*) is an introduced species escaped from aquaria and restricted to Cheshire and Lancashire, occurring mainly in ponds but also in rivers where mussels of the Unionidae family are found. This arrangement benefits the mussels, because the bitterling is a host to the larvae of the mussel which live as a parasite on the fish. It seems highly unlikely that the bitterling, a small fish seldom exceeding 10 cm (4 inches), will long survive the rigours of the British climate.

Rudd (Scardinius erythrophthalmus) *and roach* (Rutilus rutilus)

Hybridisation between these species can cause confusion but they can be distinguished (see table six), the easiest way being to look at the colour of the iris around the eye. The rudd, although absent from most

Table 6. Comparison of the Rudd and Roach

	Rudd	Roach
Length	15–30 cm	15–25 cm
Weight	100–300 gm	Up to 900 gm
	(3.50 oz–10.5 oz)	(about 2 lb)
Colour of dorsal surface	greenish	dark blue-green
Colour of sides	yellowish	silvery-blue
Colour of ventral surface	white	white
Colour of iris	gold	red

of Scotland, is common in canals and sluggish rivers, especially those choked with vegetation. The rudd occurs throughout Ireland, unlike the roach, which is absent from that country apart from the South-west and North-west.

Like the rudd, roach tend to form large shoals in slow-moving rivers. The species has always been popular with coarse anglers, who showed

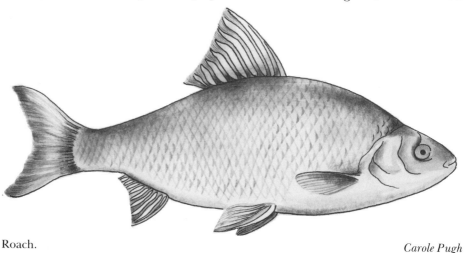

Roach.

Carole Pugh

understandable concern in the 1960s when populations were decimated by ulcerated dermal necrosis, but there has been a great improvement in recent years.

Orfe (Leuciscus idus) *and dace* (Leuciscus leuciscus)

Two other roach-like species are the introduced orfe and native dace. Roach have 42–45 scales along the lateral line, the rudd 40–45, the orfe 56–61 and the dace 49–52. The iris of both the dace and the orfe is yellowish. As in all aspects of natural history, the difficult species can only be separated by experience and by careful attention to detail.

The orfe, introduced from Europe, is found mainly in south-eastern Britain, preferring the deep waters of ponds but proving happy enough in slow-moving rivers. While dace are found throughout England, apart from parts of the south-west, they are absent from most of Wales, Scotland and Ireland. It is a true river species and is seen in shoals close to the surface of cold streams. In some parts of Britain the species is known as the dart, an accurate name for this lovely little fish with flashing silver sides and greenish-yellow fins. Spawning takes place during May and June, the yellow eggs being laid in flowing water on the stems of water plants or among gravel. During the breeding season the males have white tubercles on the head. The eggs hatch in two or three weeks and the fish reach maturity in about two years, adults occasionally reaching a length of 30 cm (12 inches).

Loaches

The stone loach (*Noemacheilus barbatus*), although absent from most of Scotland, is widespread in the rest of Britain and Ireland. This species was described in chapter two but there is also the indigenous spined loach (*Cobites taenia*), probably under-recorded due to its secretive habits; it does, however, appear to be restricted to the eastern midland region of England. The body is around 11.5 cm (4.5 inches) long and laterally compressed. There are six short barbels around the mouth which enable the species to be distinguished from the stone loach. The main point of distinction is the spine under each eye from which the spined loach gets its name. The scales are very tiny compared to those of the stone loach.

The loaches are sometimes called cat fish by anglers, but the wels (*Siluris glanis*), which has been introduced into a few ponds and reservoirs of south-eastern England, is much more cat-like in appearance.

Sticklebacks

The ubiquitous three-spined stickleback has already been described in chapter three, but the ten-spined stickleback (*Pungitius pungitius*) is also a native species and more widely distributed than is usually realised. Seldom growing longer than 7 cm (2.8 inches), this species is smaller than its three-spined relative, and is more usually found in muddy ditches and ponds. The two species never hybridise, and thus they are easily separated by counting the spines.

The eel (*Anguilla anguilla*), the only freshwater member of the family Anguillidae, was described in chapter three.

Gadidae

The Gadidae are represented by the burbot (*Lota lota*), which is indigenous in a few rivers and lakes of eastern England. It is almost entirely nocturnal, spending the day under stones or in holes in river banks.

The burbot has probably always been rare in Britain; it is now even less common than it used to be and some consider it to be extinct. Its old name was eel-pout, probably because of its large mouth, typical of most members of the cod family. The mouth shows a set of predatory teeth which it uses to good effect on invertebrates, smaller fish, and unwary anglers. The dorsal fin is divided into two, which makes it easily recognised. A mature burbot can reach a length of 1 metre (39.4 inches) and can weigh as much as 30 kg (66 lb), and it can live for more than twenty years.

The Serranidae family is represented by one estuarine species, the sea bass (*Dicentrarchus labrax*), and the Centrarchidae by three uncommon species, the large-mouthed bass (*Micropterus salmoides*), introduced in the late nineteenth century from North America, the pumpkinseed (*Lepomis gibbosus*), also introduced from North America and found only in Somerset and perhaps in Suffolk, and the rock bass (*Ambloplites rupestris*), also brought from North America into Oxfordshire.

Percidae

There are three species belonging to the Percidae in Britain, all of them fiercely carnivorous. Members of the perch family invariably have two dorsal fins, the anterior structure being spined and the posterior fin softer. The anal and pelvic fins also often have spines.

The perch (*Perca fluviatilis*) is native and widespread in Britain's slower and more weedy stretches of river, only being absent from parts of

The perch, a fiercely carnivorous inhabitant of rivers.   *John Clegg*

northern Scotland. Occasionally a few individuals are found in fast-moving water, but the larger shoals are found in the deeper reaches where they feed on invertebrates and on fish.

The ruffe (*Gymnocephalus cernua*) is also native to Britain but is almost completely confined to the midland counties of England. It looks very like the perch in outline, but whereas the perch has two very distinct dorsal fins, in the ruffe there is one long, continuous dorsal fin. The perch is also more colourful and has dark bands on the sides which contrast sharply with the yellow-green sides and pale belly, perfect camouflage for the fish as it goes hunting among the water plants and shadows cast by them. Perch can reach 40 cm (15.8 inches) but an average specimen is not much more than half this length. The plump muscular fish can weigh 1.2 kg (2 lb 10 oz) and I find it a very pleasant meal, especially if cooked in butter.

The ruffe prefers to spend much of its time feeding on the invertebrates of the bottom mud. It seldom exceeds 20 cm (8 inches) in Britain and the weight is less than 0.5 kg (1 lb 2 oz).

There are no recorded hybrids between the three species of the perch family, the third member being the zander (*Stizostedion lucioperca*), introduced to the East of Britain in the nineteenth century. Still very restricted in range, it is found in the Cambridgeshire rivers, especially the Great Ouse, and it is thought that the zander may now be established in the watershed of the River Severn. Not all anglers welcome a fiercely carnivorous fish which can reach a metre in length (39.4 inches) and possesses a pair of jaws very reminiscent of those of a pike. The favoured habitat is lakes and deep, slow-moving rivers; its British distribution is not known with any degree of accuracy.

Gobiidae

The gobies are a family of quite small fish living in the shallow seas. Fifteen species occur in Europe, but only the common goby (*Pomatoschistus microps*) is able to tolerate fresh water, and even then is seldom found far beyond the tidal reaches. It is possible to confuse the common goby with the bullhead but the former is much smaller and seldom exceeds 7 cm (2.8 inches) in length and there are also anatomical points of distinction, the most obvious being the fusion of the pelvic fins in the goby to produce a type of suction organ. This prevents the fish from being moved around by the ebb and flow of the tide; the goby is also able to hold tightly against fast-moving river water. The bullhead has, as its name implies, a much larger head and its pelvic fins are quite separate and have no ability to function as a sucker.

Miller's thumb. *Carole Pugh*

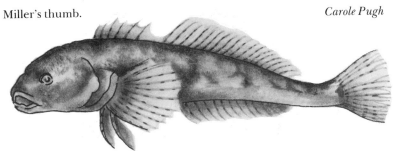

Cottidae

The freshwater bullhead (*Cottus gobio*) is the only member of this world-wide family of more than 3,000 species which is found in Britain; it was fully described in chapter two.

Mugilidae

The mullets are predominantly marine fish. They are often found in vast shoals and are distinguished by the presence of two dorsal fins and the surprising and unexplained absence of a lateral line. Three species occasionally push beyond the estuaries of British rivers, the thick-lipped mullet (*Crenimugil labrosus*), which can reach 90 cm (35.5 inches) in length, the smaller thin-lipped mullet, which seldom attains 50 cm (19.7 inches), and the golden mullet, which is of similar size.

Pleuronectidae

This marine family which includes the plaice (*Pleuronectes platessa*) are flat fishes typified by having both eyes situated on the right of the head, the left eye undertaking a startling migration during the developmental period. Occasional 'left-sided' specimens are found in the plaice and also in the dab (*Limanda limanda*); such specimens are found quite commonly in the flounder (*Platichthys flesus*). Unlike most flatfish flounders are able to tolerate fresh water and are frequently found in rivers and also in lakes which are linked to the sea. The basic colour on the left side is brown, often with a shading of green and also often with blotches of rusty red. The 'blind side' is much paler, a perfect example of counter-shading. Flounders are distinguished from plaice by a lack of ossified knobs on the head and can attain a weight of 3 kg (6 lb 10 oz) and measure up to 50 cm (19.7 inches). Most specimens found in rivers, however, are much smaller, but they are still attractive to freshwater anglers and to fish-eating birds such as the cormorant and the heron. It is to these birds that we turn in the next chapter.

Perch.   *Carole Pugh*

CHAPTER NINE

Birds of River and Marsh

SEVERAL attempts have been made to classify rivers into zones according to the bird species found along the various stretches from moorland catchment areas to the estuary.

Red throated divers, whimbrel, curlew, dotterel, ring ouzel, hen harrier, lapwing, redshank and snipe may perhaps typify the upland zone, with the dipper being found closer to the feeding stream than any of them. In areas overlooked by large stands of trees the spectacular goosander hunts for fish. As the water slows down other birds such as oyster catcher, common sandpiper, heron, grey and pied wagtail, kingfisher and reed bunting find conditions to their liking. The warblers and the water rail particularly favour the reed beds. In the sluggish areas of rivers sand martins nest in the banks and mute swans breed along the feeder streams, along with mallard, moorhen, coot and little grebe.

Any attempt to classify rivers into 'avian zones' is bound to fail, however, because of the sheer mobility of birds. There is no doubt that man's 'management' of waterways has often affected the birds, and it is surprising that we had to wait until 1974 for the enterprising British Trust for Ornithology to organise a Waterways Bird Survey.

Waterways provide a unique breeding habitat and are one of the most threatened areas of the environment. The data which have been gathered since the survey began have already done much to conserve threatened species and improve some aspects of river management. We will return to this aspect of the survey in chapter eleven.

In spite of their mobility, we will consider the birds of the rivers under the artificial but convenient headings of upland birds, birds of the middle reaches and birds of lowland rivers and estuaries.

Upland birds

High on the damp windswept moors of northern Scotland the occasional whimbrel adds its distinctive voice to that of its relative the curlew, while the mournful notes of the red throated diver can be spine-chilling on a cool spring morning. On the high hills hen harriers quarter the ground looking for hares, rabbits, voles and perhaps an unwary red grouse; dotterel strut around the climber's feet and the bell-like notes of the ring ouzel echo from the lowering cliffs. As the river tumbles and foams its way downhill dippers walk fearlessly into the torrent. If the river swirls its way through a tree-lined gorge goosanders find ideal feeding and breeding habitat. On the lower slopes snipe, redshank and lapwing also breed. This impressive list serves to underline the need for these upland areas to be fiercely protected.

Whimbrel *(Numenius phaeopus)*

Some workers have suggested that the whimbrel should be called the northern curlew, which implies a geographical distinction between the two. In fact there is a considerable area of overlap where the species occur together, as on the hills of northern Scotland and the offshore islands, where whimbrels are found at much higher altitudes than the curlew. The present British breeding population does not exceed 200 pairs but substantial numbers pass through on their way to northern breeding grounds from their African wintering areas.

The whimbrel can be distinguished from the curlew by its high-pitched whistling call of seven syllables, and by two dark bands on the crown. The bill is not so curved as the curlew's and the whimbrel is only 41 cm (16.2 inches) long compared to the curlew's average size of around 55 cm (21.7 inches). The chosen nest site, often close to an upland pool, is lined with sphagnum, the four eggs usually being incubated by the end of May unless the spring has been particularly cold. After a twenty-eight-day incubation period the chicks are often divided between the parents and the two groups feed independently; this would seem to make sense while the young are flightless and vulnerable to predators. The family joins up again once the young can fly. This 'safety first' behaviour also seems to be part of the curlew's breeding cycle, although some authorities

Left: The whimbrel's four eggs in its sphagnum-lined nest not far from an upland pool.

Michael Edwards

Opposite: The whimbrel, of which no more than 200 pairs now nest in Britain.

Michael Edwards

A curlew, largest of the British waders, seen among the coarse grass of an upland moor.
Charles Linford

believe that the female helps to tend the young for two or three weeks and then leaves the male to cope on his own for a further three weeks until the young fledge.

Curlew *(Numenius arquata)*

In contrast to the plovers, which tend to be brightly coloured, the snipes and sandpipers to which both the whimbrel and the curlew belong tend to be much more cryptically coloured and to show greater variety in bill shape. The curlew is our largest wader, easily recognised by its long downcurved bill and pale rump. Its onomatopoeic call and loud bubbling flight 'song' are both diagnostic.

For some unexplained reason the curlew has over the last hundred years or so extended its British breeding range. At one time it was a moorland nester but it is now found incubating eggs in fields alongside stretches of meadering rivers down in the flood plain. There are probably more than 60,000 breeding pairs spread throughout the whole of Britain.

There is a movement to the coast during the winter, when the population on the estuaries of Britain and Ireland may approach 250,000 due to an influx of breeding birds from northern Europe.

The diet of the curlew has been carefully investigated by Burton (1974), Goss-Gustard and Jones (1976), Glutz (1977) and others. In winter they take large numbers of marine worms and shellfish, but at other times of the year they may feed on freshwater invertebrates. They have been known to take water bugs, mayflies, caddisflies, dragonflies and freshwater shrimps as well as the occasional amphibian and fish. As with the majority of birds, the indigestible portions are regurgitated in the form of pellets.

Red throated diver *(Gavia stellata)*

Although this is our most common species of diver, there are fewer than 1,000 breeding pairs scattered around the upland lochs of Scotland and Ireland. It is debatable whether the red throated diver should be classed as an upland river bird at all, but it is a feature of the fast streams draining the soggy moors of many of the Western Isles.

There is no mistaking this 60 cm (23.6 inches) long bird in its splendid breeding plumage. The red throat patch contrasts with the dark back, grey head and white chest and belly. In winter these features disappear but the bird can still be recognised by its slim, slightly upturned bill and in flight by its humpbacked body and long thin neck held straight in front. Although red throated divers breed on upland lochs there is not likely to be enough fish in them to support adults and young, and frequent trips to the sea are therefore essential.

Hen harrier *(Circus cyaneus)*

The size of this species varies from 43 to 52 cm (16.9–20.5 inches); the males are smaller than the females. Hen harriers, as they fly slowly over the moor in search of prey, look surprisingly owl-like. In common with owls they have a facial disc which serves to focus sound on to the sensitive eardrums. Here, then, is a diurnal bird of prey which hunts by sound rather than by sight and thus specialises in the slow, almost silent flight typical of owls. Indeed this upland habitat is often shared with the short eared owl *(Asio flammeus)*. Both species, despite eating large

A hen harrier's nest, with three eggs still to hatch, among the heather of a moorland.
Michael Edwards

numbers of voles, have been blamed for reducing the efficiency of grouse shoots and were in the past mercilessly slaughtered by keepers because of it. Alas, the paranoiac fear of such hunting birds has still not disappeared although even a little reduction of pressure has allowed the hen harrier to spread from its stronghold in the Orkneys to many upland areas of Britain. More than 700 pairs now breed in Britain, but hen harriers still need special protection under Schedule one of the Birds Act, 1954–1967.

The male has a shiny grey back with easily seen black wing tips and white underparts. This plumage is so distinctive that the male alone used to be called the hen harrier and was thought to be a different species from the ring-tailed hawk, which we now recognise as his mate. She is basically brown with a white rump and with rings of black on her pale brown tail.

Red grouse *(Lagopus lagopus)*

The mainly vegetarian red grouse requires vast heather moorlands to survive, and few species can have been more fiercely protected. They are good to eat, and the problem of raising artificially high populations is eased by the fact that the species is tough, able to survive all that an upland winter can throw at it, and so sedentary that it is seldom found more than 1.5 km (0.94 mile) from its place of hatching.

163

One of the most exciting periods in a naturalist's calendar is the spring when he can wander the high hills, listening to the surging of the melt-water as ice and snow thaw and to the bubbling call of the curlew and the 'go-back go-back' display call of the red grouse. When disturbed the birds take off with a whirr of cracking wings and a 'kok-kok' alarm call before gliding back to earth and hiding in the deep heather.

This treeless habitat is often shared with the ring ouzel (*Turdus torquatus*), which is often accurately called the mountain blackbird, and which comes to Britain to breed but retreats to southern Europe and North Africa for the winter.

Goosander *(Mergus merganser)*

Those of us who criticise the regimented stands of conifers in modern plantations, often with good cause, should not assume that these offer no benefits to wildlife. The goosander is a river-based duck which requires trees for breeding and has found the maturing conifers much to its liking; from its first British nesting way back in 1871 its success has been spectacular. The first eggs were incubated in Scotland and the goosander did not breed in England until 1941.

A look at the red saw-like bill of this 62 cm (24.5 inches) long duck shows that it must be an efficient fish catcher, and salmon and trout do indeed form a significant proportion of its diet in the upper reaches of rivers. Despite strenuous efforts by fishermen to prevent its spread and

Female goosander. *Carole Pugh*

despite the fact that the goosander is not protected by law, there are now more than 2,000 pairs breeding in Britain.

A favourite nest site is in hollow trees up to 20 metres (65 feet) from the ground. After hatching, the young are so light that they are able to jump to the ground and follow their mother to the river. In the absence of trees the female goosander conceals her down-lined nest among boulders and vegetation close to the river bank. In the early days the ducklings are often given a ride on their mother's back, tucking themselves under her wings. This behaviour is also seen in the great crested grebe (*Podiceps cristatus*) and the mute swan (*Cygnus olor*).

There are few more attractive birds than the goosander; the male has a green head and black back, with the rest of the body almost white and with a delicate pink flush on the chest. The female has a pronounced crest on her chestnut-coloured head and a grey neck, the rest of the body being greyish.

Snipe *(Gallinago gallinago)*

An item headed 'Snipe Alarm' on page three of *BTO News*, March, 1983, underlines the problems faced by many riverside birds when their habitat is threatened:

> Last summer many members of the British Trust for Ornithology were out in the field looking for breeding waders in wet meadows. Preliminary results, reported by the organiser, Dr Ken Smith, show that alarmingly few snipe and redshank were discovered. Only just over 2,000 snipe were recorded performing their early display flight and less than 2,500 redshank. These figures for lowland England and Wales show just how far the wet meadow habitat has been lost to drainage for farming purposes. Many of the birds which were found lived in protected habitats like the RSPB reserves in East Anglia and Kent which held more than a third of all pairs of redshank recorded in England and Wales! The results of the survey will be used by organisations interested in conservation to show how important the remaining sites are for the British populations of these attractive birds.

Although more then 80,00 pairs of snipe still breed in Britain, this decline noted by the BTO needs to be treated seriously. Snipe are easy to count because of the unique display flight of the male, who flies around his territory in an undulating manner, vibrating the stiffened outer tail feathers to produce a bleating sound which is usually referred to as 'drumming'.

An old farmer friend once told me that snipe were able to anticipate the weather; he maintained that if the males drummed high over the moors we were in for good weather, but if they performed near the ground rain was imminent. I have often used this knowledge since and it does seem to work.

All the twenty-day incubation period of the four eggs is undertaken by the female. As soon as the young are dry, however, the clutch is usually split into two, an anti-predator strategy also practised by the whimbrel.

The snipe is 27 cm (10.6 inches) long and easily recognised by its striped crown, short legs and long bill. The sensitive bill enables snipe to reach worms and insect larvae, but some grasses and seeds are also eaten.

Redshank *(Tringa totanus)*

To the birdwatcher in the field the redshank can be a most confusing species. In flight it seems to be black and white due to broad white patches on the borders of the wings, rump and tail coverts. As soon as it lands, however, these white patches are folded and the bird appears grey-brown and blends quickly into its environment. The white flight pattern may well help the redshank to keep in station during the long migratory journeys.

The long red legs are the most obvious feature of this 28 cm (11 inch) wader, but in young birds the shanks may be yellow and this can lead to some confusion. There can be no confusion with the call, however, as the wary bird's 'tew-teuk-tew' alarm note earns it the name of 'guardian of the marsh'.

The nest is made in a dry hollow on a wet moor or marsh and lined with grass by the female. Both parents incubate the four eggs for about twenty-three days, and as soon as they are dry the young are led, despite often formidable obstacles, to the nearest river. Parent birds have been observed to help their young by carrying them between their thighs for short distances.

There are probably in excess of 50,000 breeding pairs in Britain, but there is some threat to the population due to loss of habitat. The numbers are, however, swollen in winter as migrants arrive from Iceland and Northern Europe. In breeding plumage redshanks are warm brown streaked with black, thus appearing darker than in winter. It also seems that those nesting in Iceland and other northern areas have even more attractive colours. Ornithologists recognise a northern and a southern race of redshank, our breeding birds being part of the latter population.

Lapwing *(Vanellus vanellus)*

Although the lapwing is distributed throughout Europe and Asia and no sub-species are recognised, it does seem that in Greenland and Iceland individuals in breeding dress seem slightly larger and more colourful than their British equivalent. The lapwing or peewit, being a plover, is much more territorial than the curlew or redshank, which belong to the sandpiper family. Aerial battles are common as the males

The lapwing or peewit (*Vanellus vanellus*) is a familiar bird of farmland, but it nests on moorland close to the upper reaches of rivers. Below, the eggs are hatching and, right, a lapwing chick sets out into the world. At bottom is a redshank (*Tringa totanus*) incubating its eggs.

All by Michael Edwards

Left: A dipper prepares to plunge into a stream in search of food.

Michael Edwards

Below: A heron's method of feeding is very different: it stands motionless awaiting the chance to strike at a fish with its powerful beak.

Elsie Baines

set up their moorland nesting sites during early spring. The nests are often quite close together, which serves to aggravate the clamour, each female laying four eggs in a hollow lined with grass. Both sexes incubate for a period of between twenty-four and thirty days, depending upon the weather conditions. The young leave the nest immediately they are dry and are guarded mainly by the female until they fledge, usually in the fifth or sixth week following hatching.

More than 200,000 pairs of this black and white crested wader breed in Britain, but some workers have suggested a sharp decline in some counties due not only to loss of habitat but also to the use of insecticides killing the invertebrates which the birds eat. Lapwings are around 30 cm (12 inches) long and, if viewed in clear spring sunlight, must rate as one of the most attractive species in the world. The black areas of the plumage reflect a metallic green and the under tail coverts are a delicate rusty red, and the legs are also reddish. As with the redshank there is an autumn movement down rivers to the coast, where they are joined by visitors from the colder northern areas.

Birds of the middle reaches

Few species can live close to torrential river conditions, but as we have already seen, the dipper and the grey wagtail are exceptions. Once the flow is sufficiently reduced to allow permanent pools to develop and trees to establish themselves the heron and the kingfisher can find both

Kingfishers take no account of regulations, but they can be seriously affected by Man's treatment of the rivers.   *Michael Edwards*

169

food and shelter. The shingle deposited by the winter spates provides a habitat for the common sandpiper and the oystercatcher.

Heron *(Ardea cinerea)*

The stately heron stands in its favourite river pool waiting patiently for an unwary fish, and is so successful that it still earns the jealousy of anglers. Reaching a height of 94 cm (37 inches) and having a slow deliberate flight, it was once a favourite quarry of falconers in search of food; now its leisurely flight makes it an easy target for gunmen.

A careful study of the food of the heron reveals its fondness for eels. During the struggle with a captured eel the heron's plumage becomes smeared with mucus, which would affect the efficiency of the feathers, but the heron overcomes this by having down feathers which readily break down into powder; this is spread on to the plumage. In a fascinating article in the magazine *Country-Side* of Summer, 1984, John Clegg noted how some birds have evolved combs to remove the powder and slime:

> It is perhaps not generally known that in a number of birds the nail on the middle toe of each foot is in the form of a comb. British birds which have these serrated claws are gannet, cormorant, shag, heron, bittern, black-tailed godwit, barn owl and nightjar. The structure of the comb varies between the different species; in the gannet it is little more than a series of cracks in the nail, but the bittern has a truly magnificent comb with thirty-six well-formed teeth.
>
> It will be noticed that with two exceptions—the barn owl and the nightjar—the birds are species that frequent water, either fresh or salt, and the same applies to birds in other countries that have combs. It seems fairly safe to assume that the serrated claws are in some way useful to birds that live near water and presumably they are for the purpose of cleaning the plumage after feeding on wet and perhaps slimy foods such as fish. This was confirmed in the case of the bittern by some excellent films made in the 1930s by Lord William Percy in East Anglia, illustrating the whole elaborate toilet performance in detail. The bittern, after feeding on such slimy fish as eels, when its feathers became covered in slime, rubbed its head and neck over the powder down patches on the breast, groin and upper surface of the thighs. After an interval during which the slime was disintegrated by the powder, the bird combed through the plumage with the middle toe of each foot in turn. Finally, the head and neck were rubbed to and fro over the oil-gland near the tail to restore the lustre to the feathers.

Herons, often but not always nesting in colonies, are large birds and therefore easy to count. Numbers have been accurately recorded since 1928 and about 10,000 pairs occur in Britain, though the populations are often severely reduced in bad winters. This is hardly surprising because herons breed early in the year, and are often incubating the clutch of three to five eggs as early as February.

The nest is an untidy heap of sticks, usually high in a tree but occasionally in reed beds. The male brings the nesting material and the female builds the nest, but both share the incubation period of around twenty-five days. Feeding the hungry young until they fledge seven to eight weeks later is a full-time job for both parents, and it is at this time

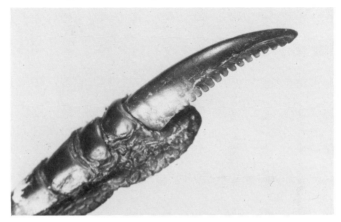

A heron's serrated claw with which it combs its feathers to remove fish slime. *John Clegg*

that they incur the wrath of anglers. Herons are usually single clutched, but occasionally a second brood is raised. British herons tend to be sedentary but are joined by continental birds for the winter, and quite large congregations may occur on the estuaries during cold weather.

Kingfisher *(Alcedo atthis)*

Like the heron the kingfisher depends upon open water for its food, and its population drops dramatically in cold winters. Few nest in Scotland, the 8,000 or so breeding pairs being concentrated in lowland England, Wales and Ireland. As its name implies, the kingfisher feeds mainly on fish and although it is only 16.5 cm (6.5 inches) long it can deal with surprisingly large prey.

Sticklebacks, minnows and bullheads figure prominently in the diet, the fish being captured in the course of a plunge-dive from a convenient overhanging branch or other perch. The prey is brought back to the perch and beaten to death before being swallowed head-first in order to prevent the operculum opening and causing the fish to block the kingfisher's gullet. A kingfisher seen carrying a fish with its head pointing out of its mouth will either be feeding young or it will be a male bird feeding his mate as part of the courtship ritual. The sexes can be distinguished by the fact that both mandibles of the male are black, while the lower mandible of the female's bill has an orange base.

No bird is so colourful as the kingfisher; its true brilliance can only be seen when in flight, or if a perched bird twists and turns in bright

171

A kingfisher in a typical pose on a branch overhanging the stream.   *Michael Edwards*

sunlight, because the colour has a double origin. Apart from the obvious colour pigments the feathers have on them small semi-transparent blocks of a waxy substance, triangular in shape, which act like prisms, breaking sunlight into a rainbow of refracted light—this is called structural colour.

Kingfishers breed in holes in the river bank and the populations are limited by hard weather and by lack of suitable nesting sites, and have also suffered alarmingly in some areas from pollution killing off the fish stocks. The six to ten white eggs are usually laid in early May on a nest of stinking fish bones at the end of a tunnel up to 1 metre (39.4 inches) long which the birds dig into the river bank. Both parents share the incubation, lasting around three weeks, and together undertake the burden of feeding the young until they can fly, which is any time between three and four weeks after hatching. The kingfishers may raise a second brood, and this may enable the population to recover quite quickly from bad winters.

Common sandpiper *(Actitis hypoleucos)*

Most stretches of river, even some of the upper reaches, have a pair of summer visiting common sandpipers breeding around the shingle beds in the surrounding greenery. Never gregarious, even on migration, sandpipers are easily recognised by their bobbing motion as they perch

172

on rocks in the river looking out for worms, insect larvae, crustaceans and molluscs. It is thought that the bobbing action may make the sandpiper difficult to see against the moving water of the river. In flight the white wing bars, white edges to the tail and shrill 'twe-we-we' call note are all diagnostic. The wing action is very stiff, and after a series of rapid wing beats the bird glides low along the river, often for a surprisingly long distance.

Sandpipers arrive from Africa early in May, although a few individuals do overwinter in southern counties of England, and by early June the clutch of four eggs is being incubated by both sexes. The young hatch in around three weeks and follow their parents downstream to the coast, the journey beginning on foot before the babies are fledged. Adults measure around 20 cm (7.9 inches) and it is thought that as many as 50,000 pairs may breed in Britain. They may well breed far enough up our rivers and streams to escape being affected by pollution; this might also be true of the oystercatcher, which is spreading its breeding range in a most encouraging manner.

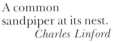

A common sandpiper at its nest.
Charles Linford

Oystercatcher *(Haematopus ostralegus)*

This conspicuous black and white bird with its pink legs and long powerful red bill is one of the most spectacular of the waders. In flight the white wing bar is unmistakable, as is the 'kleep-kleep' call uttered in flight and while feeding. At 43 cm (17 inches) oystercatchers need plenty of food to keep them going. They can make short work of cockle and mussel beds, especially in winter when the British population of around

Roosting oystercatchers on the Kent estuary in Lancashire. The Kent is one of the rivers which empties into Morecambe Bay, a haven for wildlife now under threat. *Ron Freethy*

35,000 breeding pairs can be joined by as many as 200,000 visitors from northern Europe. The flocks tend to be concentrated around the estuaries.

In winter plumage the birds have a white half collar round the throat. The breeding population has increased over the last hundred years, probably as a result of a reduction in persecution and despite the loss of suitable habitat—their favourite haunts often being swallowed up by holiday complexes built to cater for our increased leisure. Shingle beaches have been lost but the oystercatcher, and to a lesser extent the ringed plover (*Charadrius hiaticula*), have reacted by laying eggs among the river shingle beds, often close to the source of a river. Its 'piping' display call is now increasingly a welcome sound on our moorlands in springtime. The birds seem quite able to survive by changing their diet to earthworms and the abundant insect larvae.

Three eggs are laid in a scrape made in the shingle and the twenty-six-day incubation is shared by both parents. As soon as they are dry the young leave the nest; although they feed themselves they are physically protected by both parents until they can fly, which they do around thirty-five days from hatching.

Birds of lowland rivers and estuaries

Any investigation of a meandering river and its flood plain will bring regular sightings of mute swans and mallard and the occasional record of a great crested grebe. Reed buntings and sand martins are also common from the middle reaches downwards, but species normally associated with the sea will on occasions penetrate quite high upriver, usually

174

carried by the force of the tide. Dealing with all these marine species is clearly beyond the scope of this book, but some mention must be made of the cormorant, another efficient feeder which is not welcomed by the majority of anglers.

Mute swan *(Cygnus olor)*

No species is easier to count than the mute swan, which is around 150 cm (60 inches) long, and has over the centuries been kept in semi-domesticity in Britain because of its succulent flesh.

Most stretches of slow river deep enough to enable the heavy birds to take off—a good male, known as a cob, weighs up to 13 kg (28.7 lb), his mate, the pen, being lighter—provide a home for a pair of swans.

During the period 1960–1980 the population declined to between 5,000 and 6,000 pairs due to a combination of factors including cold winters, irresponsible behaviour by vandals, fatalities from flying into power lines, from pollution and from the ingestion of lead weights discarded by fishermen (see chapter eleven). This led many pessimists, the author included, to have real fears for the future of the mute swan in Britain. The results of a survey published in 1984, however, show an improvement but this should not lull us all into a false sense of security so that we fail to provide the extra protection which the species requires.

In winter the mute swans are sometimes joined by the whooper swan *(Cygnus cygnus)*, which arrives in October from its breeding grounds in Iceland, Scandinavia and Russia, usually returning during early April. Whoopers are lighter but about the same size as mute swans, hold their necks much straighter and are much more vocal. The bill is yellow and black, with the yellow area ending in a point. Mute swans mingling with the flocks can be recognised by their bills, which are black and orange.

Whoopers tend to frequent low-lying areas around rivers which flood during the winter. The Ouse Washes in Cambridgeshire are a gathering point for migratory swans. Less common visitors to these temporary marshes are Bewick swans, which also have black and yellow bills but this time the yellow patch ends bluntly. Bewicks breed in Arctic Russia and Siberia and are much smaller than the other two species, seldom exceeding 120 cm (48 inches) in length.

Mallard *(Anas platyrhynchos)*

Few stretches of river, or indeed any expanses of fresh water, will be without a pair of breeding mallards; the population in Britain is likely to exceed 50,000 pairs. The size varies from 52 to 65 cm (20.5–25.6 inches). The species has long been domesticated, and the bottle-green head and neck of the wild drake mallard and the white collar separating the neck from the purple-brown breast are well known to all birdwatchers. All male mallards, even those whose lovely plumage has been lost by interbreeding with domestic stock, can be recognised by two curly tail feathers. In winter the population is swelled by many thousands of northern immigrants, mainly from Iceland, Scandinavia and Russia.

As rivers are cleared of pollution and nature trails are set up along their banks mallards may become even more common, and great crested grebes (*Podiceps cristatus*) may begin to breed along the deeper, quieter stretches. D. H. Gantzel in a letter to *British Birds* (Vol. 71 May, 1978, pp 226–227) noted that grebes were becoming more tolerant towards disturbance by pleasure boats. We must hope that this is true and that other species follow suit.

Reed bunting *(Emberiza schoeniclus)*

We all would like to live in spacious houses overlooking a gentle meander of a river; this liking for the picturesque explains why we are losing so much marginal land around the old flood plains of our rivers. The risk of flooding is reduced by raising the river banks and removing low-lying reedbeds. Many birds, especially the water rail and dabchick,

Reed bunting.

Carole Pugh

Tree sparrows, which
sometimes take over
the riverside burrows
of sand martins.
Michael Edwards

suffered because of this loss of habitat, but the reed bunting has proved
so resilient that it is probably more common now than it has ever been.
More than 500,000 pairs breed in Britain; many are still found along
river banks but others make use of gardens and make frequent visits in
winter to bird tables, where they are often confused with house sparrows
(*Passer domesticus*). The male reed bunting has a shiny black head with an
easily visible white collar and white outer tail feathers. The female lacks
the black head markings and is thus more easily confused with a female
sparrow.

Another species often found by rivers, when it may take over the
nest of the sand martin, is the tree sparrow. This has a partial white collar
which can cause confusion with the reed bunting, but the brown crown
soon identifies it and also separates it from the male house sparrow,
which has a grey crown; both male and female tree sparrows look alike.
More than 250,000 pairs breed in Britain, but they are not usually
noticed because of the confusion with the ubiquitous house sparrow. All
three of these species described here are around 14–15 cm (5.51–5.91
inches) long.

Sand martin (*Riparia riparia*)

As March winds give way to April showers the sand martins return
from wintering under the African sun and set about re-opening their
nest holes in the sandy banks of Britain's rivers. We still have almost

177

300,000 pairs breeding in Britain, but at one time we may have had in excess of one million pairs. During 1968 and 1969 a drought in the Sahel region of Africa, through which sand martins pass on migration along with the whitethroat (*Sylvia communis*), caused the deaths of many thousands of birds. The martins will almost certainly recover, because two or three broods are raised each season and they find plenty of flies even along quite polluted rivers running near refuse tips and sewage farms.

Sand martins, which are 12 cm (4.7 inches) long, can be recognised in flight by their pointed wings and a tail which is only slightly forked. At rest the back is seen to be dull brown, while the underparts are pale. The brown breast band is clearly seen when the birds stand at the entrance to the nest hole. Nesting is colonial, the burrows—bored by both sexes— being up to 1 metre (39.4 inches) long, but usually shorter. Up to seven white eggs are laid in May on a bed of feathers and straw. Both sexes incubate the eggs for a fortnight and feed the young for three weeks until they can fly. As the summer goes on high populations of this delightful little bird soon build up.

Cormorant *(Phalacrocorax aristotelis)*

The long thin neck and heavy bill of the cormorant make it an ideal fishing machine. At 90 cm (35.4 inches) it is of similar size to the heron and has an appetite equal to that of 'Frankie', as country people call the heron. Its favourite food is the flounder, and this may well be the reason why the bird is found fishing under town bridges. Occasionally after a good meal cormorants may haul themselves on to a river bank and hold their wings out in heraldic posture. This is probably to dry out the wings, but it could, according to some workers, be an aid to digestion.

Although cormorants usually breed on sea cliffs, there are several records of inland breeding. The huge nests of sticks and vegetation are built in trees, which are often killed by the chemicals contained in the birds' droppings.

As conservation-minded individuals and local authorities increase and river footpaths are developed we must take care to leave areas of water in which wildlife can thrive without interference. This is important to plants, which are threatened by heavy feet, and to birds, which are upset by noise, but is even more vital to mammals such as the otter, which is all but extinct in many parts of Britain.

CHAPTER TEN

Riverside Mammals

AN EARLY morning walk along the river bank of a lowland English river is likely to bring one into contact with almost any one of our sixty-eight mammals. All need water to drink, and the river is often the most obvious source.

The upland catchment areas of Britain's rivers will often support red deer (*Cervus elaphus*), mountain hare (*Lepus timidus*), brown hare (*Lepus capensis*) and vast numbers of short tailed field voles (*Microtus agrestis*). Lower down the slopes rabbits (*Oryctolagus cuniculus*) graze on the lush vegetation of the water meadows and make for good hunting by red fox (*Vulpes vulpes*), stoat (*Mustela erminea*) and weasel (*Mustela nivalis*).

None of these species is uniquely associated with water and they remain unaffected by pollution, river management and human water-based activities, but there are other species which are severely affected by such factors. Three species, all native to the British Isles, which are at particular risk are the water vole, water shrew and otter.

Some of the native species have been adversely affected by introduced species whose spread along the waterways and whose operations in one way or another have been causing concern to those who earn their livelihood along our rivers. Particular concern has been caused by the presence of the brown rat, the coypu and the American mink, the first of which arrived in Britain accidentally on board ships and the other two of which were brought to Britain for the sake of their fur.

Native species

Water vole (*Arvicola terrestris*)

Despite its specific name *terrestris*, this delightful mammal is very much at home in water and is often referred to as the water rat. A close look, however, will reveal it to have the flattened face of the vole in contrast to the pointed snout and long naked tail of the rat.

'Ratty', as Kenneth Grahame called the water vole in *The Wind in the Willows*, measures 32 cm (12.8 inches), of which 12 cm (4.8 inches) is tail. It can make burrows in the earth but it prefers to make inroads into the river bank, and the entrance to its home is often under water. Unlike Victorian children, the water vole is more often heard than seen, its presence given away by a crisp splash as it dives for safety when its

A water vole at the edge of a Staffordshire brook.   *Michael Chesworth*

sensitive ears detect a human footfall. Some folk have suggested that its presence can lead to erosion of river banks, but the balanced view indicates that little if any damage is done by this animal.

Not a small animal, it can inflict a nasty bite on any potential predator. The species, especially the female, is also fierce in defence of its territory. The female establishes herself on a stretch of river bank and marks each end with her faeces, which she scents with a secretion produced in glands on her flanks.

A litter of fewer than five young, often only one or two, is born during the summer after a gestation period of around twenty-one days. The male remains close by and is often fierce in the protection of his mate and family. The young, who begin to fend for themselves when about half grown, find themselves surrounded by enemies. The brown rat may kill them and take over the burrows, many fall victims to stoats and herons near the water's edge, and others are taken by pike and by mink if they venture into the deeper water. Polluted water can also pose a problem, but the water vole seems better able to cope with pollution than is the next species to be described. Water voles do not occur in Ireland, the Isle of Man or north-western Scotland and the Outer Isles.

Water shrew *(Neomys fodiens)*

Just as the water vole is our largest vole, so can the water shrew be distinguished from other shrews by its greater size. It can vary from 7 cm to 9.5 cm (2.8 inches to 3.74 inches). The glossy black fur offers little resistance to its passage through the water and swimming efficiency is also increased by a fringe of hairs on the tail and the hind feet, those on the latter producing a webbed effect. The pale underside is another example of countershading which provides camouflage, a feature which will also be noted in the case of fish. Water shrews, despite a distinct preference for water, are able to survive very well in quite dry habitats and they occur throughout mainland Britain and also on some of the Scottish islands.

The water shrew feeds mainly on small invertebrates, especially crustaceans and insect larvae, which it finds by turning over stones and pushing its prominent snout among fringing vegetation. Water shrews do not live very long and have many predators, including pike and large

A water shrew, whose swimming prowess owes much to the hairs on its tail and hind feet.
Will Bown

trout as well as otters, mink and herons, while on dry land many fall victim to owls, foxes, feral cats, stoats and weasels. These losses are compensated for by an efficient reproductive system, the gestation period being no more than twenty-four days and three litters of up to nine young being produced each year. Many animals are used as pollution indicators, and the presence of the water shrew indicates a healthy population of invertebrates which in turn reflects the healthy state of a river.

Otter *(Lutra lutra)*

Being a large, shy animal, the otter not only requires a river relatively free from pollutants but also areas free from disturbance. These areas have been termed 'otter havens'.

A fully grown dog otter can reach 150 cm (59 inches) from head to tail and weigh up to 88 kg (194 lb). The small eyes are placed in such a position on the broad flat head that the otter can easily see objects or potential prey above it. Since it often hunts in murky water, however, the vibrissae around its mouth are sensitive to vibrations and are used to catch prey and to negotiate narrows. The ears are small and rounded, and can be closed when diving, another adaptation to an underwater life.

Otters, members of the weasel family, are of course air breathing and have to surface regularly. Their thick fur traps air bubbles, and it is these escaping and reaching the surface which betray the presence of the otter. Countryfolk call this the 'otter's chain'. The movement of a swimming otter produces a V-shaped wake which can also betray its presence. On land the animal is not quite so graceful, although its playful habits are very endearing. The legs are short and there are five toes on each webbed foot. The toes on the forefeet have short pointed claws, while the nails on the hind feet are flat. This gives otter prints a characteristic shape. Evidence of their presence can be gained by looking for their faeces, which are called spraints and are used to mark territory.

Other than in the breeding season otters are solitary and hunt alone, each animal requiring about six miles (9.6 km) of river to sustain itself. This extended territory presents one of the main difficulties in trying to re-establish otters in areas from which they have vanished. Along its stretch an otter has temporary resting places called hovers as well as more permanent holes, called holts, which offer more protection.

Regular censuses have been taken of otter populations for many years by masters of otter hunts, and these indicate that in the early 1960s a serious decline set in, from which the animal is showing no signs of recovering. Help is happily on the way and we must hope that it is not too late. The situation in the mid-1980s was lucidly summarised by Dr

Rowena Jessop in an article published in *Country-Side* in the Spring of 1985:

The initial decline in otter numbers can be correlated in time and extent with the introduction of organo-chlorine insecticides in agriculture, particularly the use of dieldrin and aldrin (Chanin and Jefferies, 1979). Subsequently, habitat alteration has denied the otter a home in many areas, where bankside cover has been removed and marshes drained in the interests of intensifying agriculture. Human disturbance constitutes an additional threat as water-based recreational pursuits become

A northern otter.
Bill Wilkinson

increasingly popular. Large parts of central and southern England are now devoid of otters. In some of the areas where they still remain, including East Anglia, the population is fragmented into small groups which gradually disappear through natural mortality.

The Otter Trust was founded in 1971 by Jeanne and Philip Wayre. Their aim was to publicise the plight of the otter and plan a campaign to safeguard the future of the otter in Britain and, where possible, throughout the rest of the world. In the early years the principles of otter husbandry were established and in 1970 Philip Wayre was credited with the first breeding of Eurasian Otters (*Lutra lutra*) in captivity in Britain since 1880. Now he can claim a unique achievement, that of breeding European Otters regularly in captivity, with a total of 53 cubs born and reared to independence since 1976. The Otter Trust led a vigorous campaign to establish legal protection for the otter and it is now protected by law in Britain under the Wildlife and Countryside Act, 1981.

However, legal protection is only one step towards safeguarding the population and the Otter Trust has become a pioneer in the field of practical otter conservation.

183

The destruction of potential otter habitat causes great concern. If the otter population should recover, many haunts would no longer be suitable and there might be a dearth of appropriate sites. The Otter Trust, together with the Otter Haven Project, have sought protection for suitable riverside habitat throughout Britain. The protected areas, otter havens, are established with the help and co-operation of the riparian landowner. In the late 1970s, the Otter Trust established over 250 otter havens in East Anglia. Further protection for otter habitat is now sought through liaison with the Water Authority. Detailed discussions of intended river works frequently result in a mutually acceptable solution which safeguards otter habitat while not compromising the requirements of the Water Authority schemes.

By 1983 population surveys carried out by Otter Trust conservation officers had revealed that the otter was still disappearing from traditionally used sites. The success of the captive breeding programme surely held the key to the future survival of the native population, through the realisation of Philip Wayre's ambition, to

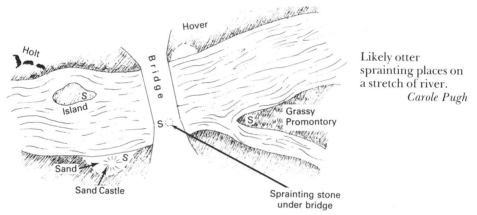

Likely otter sprainting places on a stretch of river.
Carole Pugh

release captive-bred otters into the wild. On July 5, 1983, three young otters were released on a river in East Anglia. It was the culmination of years of research and a test of all that had been learnt.

The site for the release was carefully chosen to ensure that the otters had the best possible chance of survival (Jefferies and Wayre, 1983). A river with no resident otters was an essential requirement, but ideally wild otters should be present in adjacent areas. It was also necessary to establish that the absence of otters was due to their general scarcity and not to some defect in the chosen river. The fish stocks in the selected areas were good, including eels, the otters' preferred diet, as well as rudd and roach. Several fish were caught and sent for analysis to check for levels of insecticides and other pollutants which could be passed on to otters. Water quality was judged to be high, disturbance minimal over long stretches and there was generous provision of bankside cover. This was in the form of copses, damp woodlands and reed beds; vital for the otter in providing holt sites and places in which to lie up during the day. There were no American mink (*Mustela vison*) present in the area, so removing the threat of any possible competition for food from a closely related species.

The young otters destined for release had been kept in a large semi-natural, 'quiet' enclosure, away from the public at the Otter Trust at Earsham, near Bungay in Suffolk. There they spent their first winter which coincided with their initial period

Right: The otter (*Lutra lutra*) is a shy animal and has suffered severely from disturbance in many of its haunts. Otters are now being bred in captivity and reintroduced to the wild in an attempt to reverse the serious decline in numbers which has taken place since the early 1960s. *Elsie Baines*

Overleaf: A peaceful scene on the River Stour which forms the boundary between Suffolk and Essex. It once supported a thriving otter population, but not today. *Russell Edwards*

Below: Fishermen who pay considerable sums for the privilege of fishing for salmon regard the otter as a serious rival, but in fact otters are particularly fond of eels, which eat the eggs of salmon and trout. *Michael Edwards*

of independence, a critical time for wild otters. When approximately eighteen months old, the male and two females were transferred to a release pen built on the bank of the chosen river. European otters are solitary animals when adult, with no lasting pair-bond, and the ration of one male to two females approximates to that found in the wild. The three young otters remained in the release pen for three weeks while becoming accustomed to their new environment. The pen also provided a known source of food for the otters after their release until they perfected their hunting techniques. Six days before the release the male was fitted with a harness carrying a radio transmitter, the means of monitoring the success of the project. The harness was designed to disintegrate within a few weeks, leaving the otter unencumbered (Jefferies and Mitchell-Jones, 1981; Mitchell-Jones et al., 1984). This provided invaluable information about the otters' behaviour and adaptation to the wild (Jefferies et al., 1983). The otters were monitored nightly by a team consisting of Dr Don Jefferies and Dr Tony Mitchell-Jones of the Nature Conservancy Council and the author (Otter Trust Conservation Officer) over a period of seven weeks.

On August 25, fifty nights after the release, the harness and radio were recovered from a dyke near a damp woodland frequented by the otters. There was no sign of the male. From then the monitoring of the release continued by regular surveys of the river for spraints (droppings) and footprints. The complete success of the project was confirmed on August 13, 1984, when the tracks of an otter cub following those of an adult were found in the mud under a bridge within three kilometres of the release pen. This was positive proof that at least one of the bitch otters released in 1983 had subsequently bred in the wild.

Having verified the practicability of the re-introduction policy, the Otter Trust has already organised further releases. Three otters, a male and two females, were released to the wild on July 16, 1984, and a further two otters await release in early October. It is sad that the demise of the otter would seem to be inevitable in East Anglia without such re-introductions, but the Otter Trust is determined to secure the future of the otter and the search for suitable release sites continues, for 1985 and beyond.

A typical sprainting stone under a bridge.

Carole Pugh

Sketch to show typical sprainting stone under bridge, with two spraints on the highest part of the stone.

Green Algae

Moss

187

This magnificent effort deserves to succeed, but its success depends upon extending the protection of the otter to Scotland and on applying the law we already have in England and Wales properly. At one time otter hunters occasionally caught a mink, and now that there is a move to set up 'mink hunts' there is no doubt that these would catch the occasional otter. It would be wrong to blame the hounds; in the interests of the otter, hunting mink in this manner should not be allowed. Control of mink would be far better carried out by trapping; it is possible to trap mink in cages too small for an otter to enter.

There are few more dramatic sounds than a dog otter whistling for a mate under the light of a cold February moon. After copulation and a gestation period of about nine weeks, two, sometimes three, cubs are born. The bitch otter feeds them for almost three months until they pluck up enough courage to swim. Otters have been known to live for up to twenty years, and if they could only be successfully re-established their future would be secure. Although most cubs are born in the spring there is evidence of births taking place in every month of the year in Britain. In Sweden, where the winters are much harder, the cycle is timed to ensure that the young are born in spring so that they can be old and strong enough to survive the long freezing nights of winter.

Assuming that the Otter Trust continues to be successful, naturalists will have an uphill task to persuade some anglers that otters are not going to decimate stocks of valuable game fish. It should be pointed out that otters take mainly slow-moving coarse fish and are particularly fond of eels. Since eels eat the eggs of trout and salmon it may well be that the presence of a few otters could be beneficial to the game fisherman.

A brown rat, whose ancestors arrived in Britain by ship.
Michael Chesworth

Introduced species

Brown rat *(Rattus norvegicus)*

Even though we know the health hazards posed by the common rat we cannot help but admire its adaptability. A rat is equally at home in a town sewer where it eats sewage and in a clear lowland river where it chews waterside vegetation and eats birds' eggs, young nestlings and smaller mammals.

Rats show a particular fondness for fruit and I once watched a brown rat on the banks of the River Eden in Cumbria. The autumn trees were heavy with fruit and one elder tree was overhanging the river. My attention was drawn to a rat perched precariously on a shaking branch and crunching its way through a bunch of purple berries, the sticky juice splattered on the animal's fur. Suddenly, either by accident or, as I suspect, by design, the rat dropped into the river and swam away downstream.

Brown rats have a well-ordered social structure and the dominant

A brown rat swimming in a Dorset river.
Will Bown

individuals get first choice of burrows, food and mates. They recognise each other by scents called pheromones, but the aggressiveness seen in the high population in town warehouses is tempered in country rats which have settled down to life along the rivers, where they do surprisingly little damage.

Rattus norvegicus arrived in Britain in the late eighteenth century on board trading ships and is recognised by its pointed muzzle and long scaly tail, the head and body occasionally reaching 28 cm (11 inches), males tending to be rather larger than the females. Unlike the tail of the mouse, the rat's tends to be shorter than the head and body length. The fur is brown on the dorsal surface, with the ventral area being paler. Compared to the much darker black rat *(Rattus rattus)*, which came to Britain on ships carrying the crusaders home from the Middle East, brown rats have smaller eyes and ears; the latter are hairy, those of the black rat being naked.

189

The life span is less than two years, but a continuous breeding cycle can allow high populations to build up. After a gestation period of just over three weeks a litter of up to eight young is born, and the babies are weaned in a further three weeks. Females are able to breed at eleven weeks.

The brown rat is an attractive animal, despite its ugly reputation, but there is no doubt that it needs to be vigorously controlled, as do the final two animals to be described in this chapter.

North American mink (*Mustela vison*)

The European mink (*Mustela lutreola*) has never been native to Britain and is smaller than the North American mink, which was brought to Britain when the fur industry was thriving in the 1920s. Mink farms were being set up from 1929 onwards, and these crafty little members of the weasel family were soon escaping into Britain's rivers, where they found ample food and, even more significantly, few predators. It obviously takes time for substantial populations to build up and for a time nobody worried about these fierce escapees; the Fur Breeding Association made soothing noises.

River keepers noted successful breeding of mink on the River Teign in Devon in 1956, by which time sightings were becoming far too common on the same river and along the streams of Dartmoor and the Devon Avon. By 1960 fears were being expressed by those watching the Hampshire Avon and Test, where substantial numbers of trout were being eaten as well as chickens, wild fowl and game birds, especially pheasants. By 1965 as many as 200 mink were being trapped or shot each year, and by 1980 the number being killed had risen sharply to well over 2,000 and was still rising. By this time mink were being blamed for everything which went wrong on a river, and the time was ripe for an in-depth unbiased survey of the American mink.

Although some farmed animals are inbred to produce saleable colour variants, most wild specimens are dark brown. Males are almost twice the size of the females and a good male specimen can reach a total length of almost 70 cm (27.6 inches); most animals found in the wild are much smaller than this, so confusion with the otter is highly unlikely.

From the limited data available it would seem that the breeding season begins during February, but it is difficult to establish the precise gestation period because of a delayed implantation, which means that the fertilised egg is kept in the uterus wall before beginning its development. Although up to sixteen young have been recorded in a single litter the usual number is only five or six. These are weaned after eight weeks, and the following year the young mink breed for the first time. Although it is not known just how long mink can survive in the wild, it may be as long as ten years. It is certain that they can outbreed the otter and also that they do a great deal more damage, both to wildlife and to farm stocks, than the larger species.

Some workers, notably Ian Linn and Paul Chanin (*New Scientist*, 2 March, 1979), have suggested that the potential nuisance value of the mink has been overstated and that it may settle down to become a part of our country scene not requiring any form of control. Those of us who would like to see the return of the otter and have a wish to preserve fish stocks and to search for crayfish under stones want some control.

One thing which we must all accept is that the species is far too well established and too resilient for us to be able to eradicate it. The only cost-and-time-effective method of control is by trapping. Mink are very inquisitive animals and cannot resist entering cage traps, especially those sited near weirs on rivers or in holes in banks or hollow logs. The best traps are constructed of 2.5 cm (1 inch) wire mesh of not less than 14 gauge and are baited with rotten meat or fish. A lazy farmer who has insecure poultry buildings will be sure to have occasional visits from the acrobatic mink, which is mainly nocturnal and has proved capable of squeezing through the narrowest of gaps.

Coypu (*Myocastor coypus*)

Like the mink, the coypu was brought to Britain in the 1920s for its fur, which sold under the name of nutria. When the Second World War started many fur farms were closed down and a few sentimentalists released coypu into the fens; by 1943 they were already causing damage in Norfolk and Suffolk. In 1960 the population was estimated to be around 200,000 and their burrowing activities were causing erosion of many river banks and were creating severe flooding.

Desperate measures were needed; the severe winter of 1962–63 helped to reduce numbers and this was followed by an intense trapping programme.

The coypu, which is native to South America, is a large semi-aquatic rodent. A full-grown male can weigh more than 80 kg (176.5 lb) and measure 1 metre (39.4 inches). Imagine a colony of these animals burrowing into river banks and tearing out the roots of aquatic plants which help bind the soil. Their diet is almost exclusively vegetarian, although they are reported to eat freshwater mussels if they come across them.

Female coypus are able to breed from the age of six months, and as many as twelve embryos are implanted in the uterus although only six or so of these usually develop. The gestation period has been estimated at

191

between 130 and 135 days, and the young are suckled for the first six or seven weeks. Despite this, many are able to chew vegetation within three weeks of their birth. Because of their large size coypus have found few predators in Britain, which explains why their populations build up so quickly.

Not all the activities of the coypu can be condemned. It often clears away dominant species such as meadowsweet, fen rush, and the great hairy willowherb, leaving open areas of mud on which birds can nest and perhaps also feed and into which sweet flag, purple loosestrife and other colourful plants are able to move. Those who wish to protect the coypu, however, are clutching at straws. The animal must not be allowed to spread. One first priority must be to conserve our native wildlife, which has never been more under threat than at the present time.

CHAPTER ELEVEN

River Conservation

THERE is a well-known saying that the oceans are the sinks of the world and that all forms of pollution end up in the marine environment. When we realise that the main route to the sea is via the river systems it is apparent that the majority of pollutants must travel along freshwater highways.

If we are to protect our rivers, both for the good of wildlife and for our leisure, we must understand the sources of pollution and work out management plans accordingly. Some of the problems can be considered under seven headings: acid rain, the agricultural industry, fishing, both legal and illegal, fish farming, sewage input, river management, and finally recreation and wildlife.

Acid rain

It is interesting to look at a book published in the Britain of 1872, at a time when our blackened cities were earning their name as the workshops of the world. This book, *Air and Rain: The Beginnings of a Chemical Climatology*, made the point that acid fumes from burning coal could damage buildings and delicate plants such as lichens.

These days we cannot see the smoke, but acids (mainly sulphuric but also nitric) are still produced by burning fossil fuels. High chimney stacks—they used to be called soot-pokes—only direct the fumes away from the town into the next county, or in periods of strong wind into another country. Scandinavia is suffering particularly badly from the acid rain carried from western Europe. If anything, heavy snow brings even greater problems because when it thaws heavy loads of acid are carried into the rivers and lakes.

Acidity is measured on the pH scale which runs from 0 to 14; pH 7 is neutral, while anything above 7 is alkaline and levels below 7 are acidic. Normal rainwater picks up carbon dioxide and is usually a little below pH 5.6, but serious effects are noticed on living organisms when levels begin to fall lower than this. Experimental work has shown that the development of brown trout is halted when the acid level reaches pH 5.0, and at pH 4.5 the fry die. Some molluscs and crustaceans as well as salmon, trout, char, stonefly and mayfly larvae find pH 5.5 difficult, and once the levels fall below this they die. Levels below this are often found in British rivers. Perch and pike cope with levels above pH 5.0 and eels can handle levels as low as pH 4.3, but beyond this it is usually only sphagnum moss which is able to survive.

Obviously if there is no food then the bird life also declines, especially those birds which rely entirely on fish. The osprey (*Pandion haliactus*) and goosander will be particularly at risk. When the fish are killed before the tough invertebrates such as the water louse (*Asellus*) these may temporarily show a remarkable boom in population as the predation pressure is removed. Mallards, teal (*Anas crecca*) and goldeneye

Dipper.
Carole Pugh

(*Bucephala clangula*) gather to feast on this unexpected bonanza and this assembly of birds gives a false impression of the health of water. As the acidity of the water increases still further the invertebrates die, spelling disaster for the dipper which relies totally upon river invertebrates for its food.

Increasing acidity has another even more dangerous effect, and that is to release metals, particularly aluminium and mercury, into solution; these quickly enter the food chains and destroy fish, birds and mammals which are at the top of the chain.

Two factors are, I feel, interfering with the reduction of acid levels.

One is the commonly held belief that there is no solution, which is just not true; the answer is simple, it just costs money. The other is the mistaken view that industrial gases are the only cause for increasing acid levels.

The conservation group Greenpeace expressed their views early in 1984:

> Government statements that 'there is no evidence of large-scale damage in the UK caused by acidification' gloss over the fact that there has been no research to look for large-scale damage. A well-respected researcher in this field, Dr Unsworth, of the Institute of Terrestrial Ecology, has recently stated that he estimates the cost of crop damage in the UK at £200 million a year. 'Yield losses are likely to be between 5 and 10 per cent in the worst hit areas. If they had been any higher than this we would have picked them up by now. The problem is that the effects of sulphur pollution are generally sub-clinical and generally produce no obvious symptoms.'
>
> The £200 million is for crop losses only, and does not take account of lake degradation, corrosion of buildings and materials, and potential forest damages. The OECD has noted that a European reduction of SO_2 by 37 per cent would achieve savings in environmental destruction of the same order as the cost of the desulphurisation machinery. As research throws up more detail about the scope and long term effects of acidification, it seems likely that substantial economic savings will be accrued by limiting the emission of sulphur and nitrogen oxides.
>
> Greenpeace wants the application of Best Available Technology to the reduction of sulphur and nitrogen oxides from all sources, whether large emission sources, vehicle exhausts, oil refineries or industrial smelters.
>
> Best Available Technology means the widespread use of Flue Gas Desulphuris-ation on large-scale emission sources, using regenerative methods that produce gypsum, sulphur, or sulphuric acid as the end-product of the smoke-cleaning system; a rapid move towards lead-free petrol, with the intention of fitting tricatalytic converters to all vehicle exhausts; an intelligent fuel supply system that routes high-sulphur fuel to desulphurised plant and restricts low-sulphur fuel to small users who could not afford FGD; and the use of desulphurisation techniques where necessary to reduce the sulphur content of coal and oil before combustion.

It would seem to most conservationists that Greenpeace have a valid point and that it is short-sighted of the British government not to spend money on the lines suggested. To blame only rain emissions for increased acid levels, however, is both naive and dangerous. We must also cast a suspicious eye at the increasing number of conifer forests.

When water runs through the needle-like conifer leaves it absorbs acidic material from the leaves and becomes even more acid. In deciduous woodlands the old practice was to fell trees, trim off the branches and burn the unwanted twigs to produce potash which was dissolved by rainwater and washed into the earth, where it neutralised any acid present. This is no longer done on a large scale and the combination of acid rain and forest run-off dissolves the shells of aquatic invertebrates and causes much other damage; the river-based food chain is disrupted. If our wildlife is to be preserved both these problems must be solved.

The agricultural industry

In the early chapters of this book the problem of sewage creating a huge biochemical oxygen demand was discussed. Equally problematical in some areas is the excrement slurry running off farms into rivers, a problem which becomes acute when animals are kept in 'factory units' rather than being allowed to graze freely over several acres. When animals are grazing in open fields their excrement can act as a fertiliser and what little is carried into streams following rain is likely to do more good than harm, but concentrated sewage from several farms where cattle or pigs are kept in enclosed buildings and the slurry piped into tanks can kill a river very quickly indeed, especially in the hot days of summer when the water volume is low. The majority of farmers appreciate this problem just as much as conservationists, but the occasional profit-motivated individual will cut his costs and time as much as possible, whatever the effects on what he sees as a distant environment.

Stricter control of these mavericks is essential; indeed, the water authorities already have the legal muscle to prevent levels of soluble nitrates rising in rivers which are used for drinking water. This soluble nitrate level is still below danger levels in British rivers, but it is much higher than it was in the 1940s.

Some farms flush manure down the drains and spread artificial nitrates on the fields. In rain the artificial fertiliser dissolves more easily than natural excrement. It would solve many problems, both financial and environmental, if slowly dissolving manure was used on the fields.

The use of agrochemicals and increased drainage of marginal land is perhaps the most worrying problem faced by wildlife today. We already produce more food than we need, and it is perhaps time we considered the beauty of the countryside as an essential commodity for which we are prepared to pay. Is it fair that the Arts Council grant should be almost ten times that of the Nature Conservancy Council?

Insecticides have been in use since the late 1950s, and the effect on some birds at the top of the food chains has been disastrous, despite the banning of many chemicals whose use has been seen to be dangerous. Peregrines (*Falco peregrinus*) and sparrowhawks (*Accipiter nisus*) were particularly affected by the DDT-based chemicals aldrin and dieldrin. On the face of it the birds should not have been affected because the substances are no more toxic than aspirin, but it has been found that whereas aspirin is eliminated quickly from the body, the insecticides are retained and build up in the body fat. These reserves of fat are drawn upon by both sexes in the winter and by the females in the spring when they start to develop a clutch of eggs. As a result of the concentration of chemicals birds die at these times, and many eggs are laid with such thin

Evidence of a polluted river: litter caught up in the branches beside the River Roch at Crimble, near Rochdale, after a March flood.   *Robert Smithies*

shells that they fail to survive the weight of an incubating bird.

It might appear that aquatic wildlife would suffer less from chlorinated hydrocarbon poisoning because of the diluting effect of the water. In fact the reverse is true because these animals have to extract their oxygen from the water, and as this gas is not very soluble large volumes of water have to be filtered through the respiratory organs. Any substances soluble in fat, including chlorinated hydrocarbons, will soon build up to lethal levels, and the poison will be passed up the food chain to grebes, herons, fish-eating ducks and aquatic mammals.

Obviously farmers must be allowed to protect their crops, but continual environmental monitoring needs to be carried out and the search for safer alternatives needs to be continued.

Fishing

Angling is the most popular sport in Britain today, and is probably the oldest form of hunting. Hooks almost identical in design with present-day fishhooks but made of flint and bone have been found by archaeologists and dated to the stone age. Fish farming is not a recent invention, but freshwater fishing for food has now been superseded by the art of angling for sport. On the whole naturalists and anglers get along well and many river folk share both hobbies.

197

There are, however, three aspects which always provoke controversy, the danger of discarded fishing tackle, unscrupulous removal of supposed fish predators, often on unfounded suspicions, and illegal poaching.

Much has been written about the dangers of nylon fishing line, often with lead shot on it, when it is thrown away by careless anglers. This soon becomes coated with green alga and its gritty feel encourages wildfowl, especially swans, to swallow the material literally hook, line and sinker.

Eager to obtain grit which when it reaches the gullet helps to grind up the food prior to digestion and absorption into the blood stream, the birds swallow the fishing line and with it the lead shot. Any hooks stick in the gullet and bring about a slow and horrible death; the tangles of nylon block the digestive tract and cause death that way; or the lead causes blood poisoning which can also lead to death.

Clearly some anglers need to take more care, although the sensible ones will quite rightly reject my implied criticism. We really need a fishing line which is bio-degradable, and we also need a non-toxic alternative to lead shot. Both these products are available, but anglers are resisting their use. They can hardly be blamed for their resistance since the alternatives are more expensive; instead of trying to force anglers to be philanthropic, naturalists should be applying pressure on manufacturers to produce more of the alternatives so that the price of these comes down; their profit margins would soon revert to normal. A government grant might very well provide the much-needed incentive.

Game fishermen are usually less likely to leave lead shot behind them, but nylon line is still a problem along some of Britain's most expensive rivers. Those paying high fees for fishing are also much less tolerant of birds such as heron, goosander, cormorant and osprey, often taking the law into their own hands. Naturalists are perfectly entitled to ask whether a bird fishing a river to stay alive has not more right to be there than an angler fishing merely for sport, and with a warm meal and a bed to return to.

Overfishing at sea and along rivers, as well as the effects of acid rain and other forms of pollution, have reduced salmon and sea trout from the food for everyman that they were in the middle ages to a luxury item. With high prices to be gained from hotels, and no questions asked, salmon poaching is now big business in Britain.

The problem was highlighted in a publication *Salmon Conservation— a New Approach*, published in 1983 by the National Water Council, which made the point that it was impossible to distinguish between a poached salmon and one taken legally or raised in a fish farm. It is proposed to get round this difficulty of identification by issuing each legitimate fisherman with tags to mark the salmon he catches; any fish not so marked would be declared illegal and its possessor would be liable to prosecution. Tagging would prove an expensive operation, but one probably necessary if wild salmon stocks are to be protected. The author would like to see this legislation brought in, but combined with a temporary ban on salmon fishing on rivers and in estuaries. Eventually farmed salmon will bring down the price, and the organised gangs of poachers will no longer have the price incentive.

Some idea of the scale of these poaching activities was given by Warwick Ayton, fisheries officer of the Welsh Water Authority, to Brian Jackman of the *Sunday Times* in July, 1983:

> Poaching used to be a cottage industry, but no longer. Nowadays it's big money. On a good night a gang can get away with more than £2,000 worth of salmon. That is why it has attracted some real villains . . . Their intelligence is good; they know exactly where and when to strike.

Fish farming

There are two aspects to consider with regard to fish farming; firstly there are hatcheries producing fry to stock rivers and lakes, and secondly

Cromwell's Bridge on the River Hodder in Lancashire, a river which is as yet unmanaged.
Ron Freethy

there are establishments geared to extending the period of protection and to producing fish for food.

The most vulnerable period in the life of the fish is at the egg stage; the fish farmer reduces chance to a minimum by artificially fertilising the eggs from captured stock. As the eggs are fertilised they swell and after a day or two a protective membrane develops, the fish farmer meanwhile ensuring that the eggs receive a constant supply of fresh, well oxygenated water, that an even temperature is maintained, and that dead eggs are removed. Within a month the hatched fry are placed in ponds, but there is still need for great care. With trout there is soon an obvious difference in size and they have to be graded, otherwise large specimens will eat their smaller companions.

The young fish are eventually sold to anglers who wish to stock their stretch of river, the fact that trout are territorial ensuring that this method works well. The brown trout (*Salmo trutta*) and the rainbow trout (*Salmo gairdneri*) are both raised in this manner, but the latter species is the one favoured by farms geared to the production of food. The rainbow trout is a native of North America and can reach a weight of 16 kg (35.3 lb).

The usual design of this type of farm involves the diversion of the waters of a swift, unpolluted stream into a series of shallow artificial ponds which can be easily drained to remove fish. The occupants of these ponds are then given protein-rich food which promotes their growth so

A mill stream on the River Esk at Ravenglass, Cumbria. Man has made use of rivers in various ways for many hundreds of years, harnessing the power of water and managing the waterways for transport.
Ron Freethy

that within two years fleshy marketable fish are ready for market. Some carp are also raised in Britain, and many farmers have turned their attention to the production of salmon.

Sewage farms

The problems caused by too much sewage have been discussed in earlier chapters, but the point must be made that the treatment of effluent is now much more efficient than it once was and our rivers are cleaner than in the past. The Thames, for example, is now a living river instead of an open sewer and wildlife is returning to reaches that used to be dead.

Sewage reaching the works is first screened to remove plastic, wood, rags and other debris before passing into detritus tanks where grease and oil is trapped by what are vulgarly called scum boards. Solid matter settles to the bottom, to be periodically dredged out and placed in digestion tanks or spread over the surrounding land, where it acts as an effective fertiliser. As it decays heat is generated, which means that sewage works are always warmer than the surrounding area and therefore contain more food in winter. The birds appreciate this, and ornithologists find areas around sewage farms wonderful places to watch. Common species such as gulls, redshank, snipe and pied wagtail roost here and rarities such as the green sandpiper (*Tringa ochropus*) and spotted crake (*Porzana porzana*) are more likely to appear on an old sewage farm than anywhere else. Modern sewage treatment works are sited largely underground, and their sterile grass banks are nowhere near so attractive to birds, although the aesthetic appeal of the countryside is obviously safeguarded by hiding the processes of sewage treatment.

The liquid portion is treated to an aeration process which helps to digest the effluent and a period of biological action by bacteria forms part of the scheme. The treated water is at the end released into a river. Most works manage to remove ninety per cent of the contaminants, except after heavy rain when the storm water overloads the system and some untreated sewage does sometimes seep into the river. Larger numbers of more efficient treatment works are constantly being built, and our rivers now have considerably less sewage in them than was the case ten years ago.

River management

Until very recently this heading should have read river mismanagement, for over the past fifty years Britain's watercourses have been subject to what amounts to a rape of wildlife. Streams have been straightened, deepened and embanked with the laudable object of

201

A marsh fritillary, a butterfly of damp moorlands which is now largely confined to areas of western and south-western Britain.
Michael Edwards

preventing flooding, but with an unforgivable degree of 'over-kill'. Tree-lined meanders have gone, leaving sterile channels devoid of all cover; a little thought would have left alder, willow and many of the herbs on which the animal life depends. The presence of plants would have increased the oxygen levels of the water, giving the water the sparkle that only rich and varied wildlife can give.

We are moving in the right direction, but until conservation is part of any river management plan there will still be loss of unique habitat. The water authorities have to satisfy both the Ministry of Agriculture and the ratepayers that they are carrying out their task as economically as possible, but the increasingly important question to be asked is 'What price wildlife?' How do we put a price on a family of coots? How much is it worth to retain an old mill stream? What would you pay to sit close to a bank of common spotted orchids and to watch a marsh fritillary butterfly flexing its wings in the early morning sun? Is the sight of a skylark's clutch of eggs worth fighting for?

Sooner or later we will have to tackle this thorny problem, for the sake of generations yet unborn.

Recreation and wildlife

To the river naturalist the term 'water-based recreation' represents something of a mixed blessing. Anglers, boaters and walkers need clean tree-lined rivers with weedy bays to enjoy their hobbies to the full. As leisure time increases there will be more pressure to clean up the rivers, and once this has been done there will be more pressure on the wildlife.

Pleasure boaters will want weeds controlled, walkers will demand more access to the river banks and anglers will press for more separation from other folk; and there will be some who point out that wildlife needs more freedom from anglers.

There is an answer. Flood levels could be controlled by 'managing' one bank of the river, and here is an ideal spot for a footpath overlooking the tree-lined bank opposite, which could be left in its natural state.

The more people using an area, the more sewage will have to be disposed of, and the phosphates and nitrates which this contains can cause problems. The associated enrichment of the water brings an increase in vegetation and watercourses can become overgrown; eventually algae grow so strongly in the enriched water that they block out the light to water plants and these can no longer survive in what begins to look like thin pea soup. This is a particular problem in areas of enclosed water such as canals and the Norfolk Broads. Some water authorities have already begun to counteract this threat by installing equipment to remove mineral salts, especially phosphates, from the effluent before it is discharged into a watercourse. There is now more willingness on the part of authorities to consider wildlife.

Many tiny inlets such as one finds in a river bank that has not been 'managed' for flood prevention are ideal havens for wildlife; the deeper pools are suitable for anglers. A number of no-go areas, cut off by streams, could be set aside for wildlife alone. Many would say that these ideas are Utopian, but the higher we aim the more we shall achieve.

The nest and eggs of the skylark.
Michael Edwards

Bibliography

Angel, Heather. *The World of a Stream*. Faber, 1976.

Bagenal, T. B. *Identification of British Fishes*. Hulton, 1973.

Beedham, G. E. *Identification of the British Mollusca*. Hulton, 1972.

Belcher, H., and Swale, E. *A Beginner's Guide to Freshwater Algae*. H.M.S.O., 1976.

Bone, Q., and Marshall, N. B. *Biology of Fishes*. Blackie, 1982.

Brinkhurst, R. O. *A Guide to the Identification of British Aquatic Oligochaeta*. Freshwater Biological Association Scientific Publication No. 22, 1963.

British Waterways Board. *The Future of Waterways*. H.M.S.O., 1964.

British Waterways Board. *The Facts about the Waterways*. H.M.S.O., 1965.

British Waterways Board. *Leisure and the Waterways*. H.M.S.O., 1967.

Burton, Maurice. *Mammals of the Countryside*. Wheaton, 1960.

Buxton, E. J. M. The inland breeding of oyster catcher in Great Britain. *Bird Study* 20, 1961, pp. 127–140.

Chanin, P. R. F., and Jefferies, D. J. The decline of the otter Lutra lutra in Britain: An analysis of hunting records and discussion of causes. *Biol. J. Linnean Soc.*, 10, 1978, pp. 305–328.

Clapham, A. R., Tutin, T. G., and Warburg, E. F. *Flora of the British Isles*, 3rd Edition. Cambridge University Press, 1981.

Clegg, John (ed). *Pond and Stream Life in Colour*. Blandford, 1963.

Clegg, John. *The Freshwater Life of the British Isles*. Warner, 1965.

Clegg, John. The medicinal leech. *Country-Side Magazine*, Spring 1984.

Clegg, John. *The British Naturalists' Guide to Ponds and Streams*. Crowood Press, 1985.

Corbet, P. S., Longfield, C., and Moore, N. W. *Dragonflies*. Collins New Naturalist series, 1960.

Dowdeswell, W. H. *Practical Animal Ecology*. Methuen, 1959.

Elliott, J. M., and Humpesch, U. H. *A Key to the Adults of the British Ephemeroptera*. Freshwater Biological Association, 1983.

Ellis, E. A. *British Freshwater Bivalve Mollusca*. Linnean Society, 1978.

Engelhardt, W. *The Young Specialist Looks at Pond Life*. Burke, 1973.

Freethy, Ron. *The Making of the British Countryside*. David and Charles, 1981.

Freethy, Ron. *How Birds Work*. Blandford, 1982.

Freethy, Ron. *The Naturalists' Guide to the British Coastline*. David and Charles, 1983.

Freethy, Ron. *Man and Beast—a Natural and Unnatural History of British Mammals*. Blandford, 1983.

Freethy, Ron. *British Birds in their Habitats*. Crowood Press, 1985.

Freethy, Ron. *The River Mersey*. Terence Dalton, 1985.

Frost, W. E., and Brown, M. E. *The Trout*. Collins New Naturalist series, 1967.

Fryer, Geoffrey. *The Parasitic Copepoda and Branchiura of the British Freshwater Fishes*. Freshwater Biological Association, 1982.

Goodden, Robert. *British Butterflies: A field guide*. David and Charles, 1978.

Hammond, C. O. *The Dragonflies of Great Britain and Ireland*. Curwen, 1977.

Harris, J. R. *An Angler's Entomology*. Collins, 1952.

Haslam, S., Sinker, C., and Wolseley, P. British water plants. *Field Studies* 4, 1975. pp. 243–351.

Hickin, N. E. *Caddis Field Study Books.* Methuen, 1952.

Hickin, N. E. *Caddis Larvae.* Hutchinson, 1967.

Hudson, C. T., and Gosse, P. H. *The Rotifera or Wheel-Animalcules,* 2 vols. Longmans, Green, 1886 with an 1889 supplement.

Hynes, H. B. N. *A Key to the Adults and Nymphs of the British Stone-flies (Plecoptera).* Freshwater Biological Association Publication No. 17, 1958.

Hynes, H. B. N., Macan, T. T., and Williams, W. D. *A Key to the British Species of Crustacea: Malacostraca.* Freshwater Biological Association Scientific Publication No. 19, 1960.

Imms, A. D. *Insect Natural History.* Collins New Naturalist series, 1947.

Isaac, P. C. G. (ed). *River Management.* Maclaren and Sons, 1967.

Jefferies, D. J., and Wayre, P. Re-introduction to the wild of otters bred in captivity. *Journal of the Otter Trust,* 1983, pp. 20–22.

Jermy, A. C., Arnold, H. R., Farrell, L., and Perring, F. H. *Atlas of Ferns of the British Isles.* Botanical Society of the British Isles and British Pteridological Society, London, 1978.

Jones, J. W. *The Salmon.* Collins, 1959.

Kimmins, D. E. *Plecoptera. Handbook for the Identification of British Insects.* Royal Entomological Society, London, 1950.

Kimmins, D. E. *A Revised Key to the Adults of the British Species of Ephemeroptera.* Freshwater Biological Association Publication No. 15, 2nd revised edition, 1972.

Laidler, Liz. *Otters in Britain.* David and Charles, 1982.

Leopold, L. B., and Davis, K. S. *Water.* Life Science Library, Time-Life Books, 1966.

Longfield, Cynthia. *The Dragonflies of the British Isles.* Warne, 1949.

Lovegrove, Roger, and Snow, Philip. *River Birds.* Columbus Books, 1984.

Macan, T. T. *A Key to the Nymphs of the British Species of Ephemeroptera.* Freshwater Biological Association Scientific Publication No. 20, 1961.

Macan, T. T. *Freshwater Ecology.* Longmans, 1966.

Macan, T. T., and Worthington, E. R. *Life in Lakes and Rivers.* Collins, 1968.

Maclean, Norman. *Trout and Grayling—An Angler's Natural History.* Black, 1979.

McMillan, Nora F. *British Shells.* Warne, 1973.

Mann, K. H., and Watson, E. V. *A Key to the British Freshwater Leeches.* Freshwater Biological Association Publication No. 14, 1954.

Marchant, J. H., and Hyde, P. A. Aspects of the distribution of riparian birds on waterways in Britain and Ireland. *Bird Study* 27, 1980, pp. 183–202.

Meadows, B. S. Kingfisher numbers and stream pollution. *Ibis* 114, p. 443, 1972.

Mellanby, H. *Animal Life in Fresh Water.* Methuen, 6th edition, 1963.

Mills, D. H. *An Introduction to Freshwater Ecology.* Oliver and Boyd, 1972.

Mosely, M. E. *The British Caddis Flies (Trichoptera).* Routledge, 1949.

National Water Council. *Salmon Conservation—a new approach.* National Water Council, 1983.

Netboy, Anthony. *Salmon: The world's most harassed fish.* Deutsch, 1980.

Newdick, Jonathan. *The Complete Freshwater Fishes of the British Isles.* Black, 1979.

Palmer, M., and Newbold, C. *Wetland and Riparian Plants.* Nature Conservancy Council, 1983.

Parslow, J. *Breeding Birds of Britain and Ireland.* Poyser, 1973.

Perring, F. H. *The Flora of Changing Britain.* Classey, 1974.

Perring, F. H. Wetland flora in danger. *Conservation Review* 13. Society for the Promotion of Nature Reserves, 1976.

Platts, W. Carter. *Grayling Fishing.* Black, 1939.

Pritt, T. E. *The Book of the Grayling.* Goodall and Suddick, 1888.

Quigley, Michael. *Invertebrates of Streams and Rivers: A key to investigation.* Arnold, 1977.

Read, D. M. *Gammaridae (Amphipoda) with a Key to the Families of British Gammaridae.* Linnean Society of London, Synopses of the British Fauna, 1944.

Reynoldson, T. B. *A Key to the British Species of Freshwater Triclads.* Freshwater Biological Association Scientific Publication No. 23, 1967.

Righyni, Reg. *Grayling.* MacDonald, 1968.

Roberts, John. *The Grayling Angler.* Witherby, 1982.

Rolt, H. A. *Grayling Fishing in South Country Streams.* Sampson, Low, 1901.

Sankey, J. *A Guide to Field Biology.* Longmans, 1958.

Schmitt, Waldo L. *Crustaceans.* David and Charles, 1973.

Smith, A. E. The impacts of lowland river management. *Bird Study* 22, 1975, pp. 249–254.

Step, Edward. *Shell Life: An introduction to British Mollusca.* Warne, 1945.

Tutin, T. G. *Umbellifers of the British Isles.* Botanical Society of the British Isles, 1980.

Walton, W. C. *The World of Water.* Weidenfeld and Nicolson, 1970.

Ward, H. B., and Whipple, G. C. *Freshwater Biology.* Wiley, 1959.

Wheeler, Alwyne. *Key to the Fishes of Northern Europe.* Collins, 1978.

Whitton, Brian. *Rivers, Lakes and Marshes.* Hodder and Stoughton, 1979.

Williams, E. G. How to begin the study of freshwater algae. *Country-Side Magazine,* Autumn, 1967.

Willoughby, L. G. *Freshwater Biology.* Hutchinson, 1976.

Youngman, R. E. Great crested grebes breeding on rivers. *British Birds* 70, 1977, pp. 44–45.

Whooper swan,
Bewick's swan
and mute swan.
Carole Pugh

Index

Illustrations in bold type

A

Acentria nivea, 136
Acid rain, 193–196
Acutipala maxima, see Cranefly
Aeshna grandis, see Dragonfly,
  brown hawker
Aeshna juncea, 125
Agapetus fuscipes, 135
Agrion virgo, 123
Agriotypus armatus, 137
Alder, common, 84
Alderfly, **132,** 134, **134,** 137
Algae, freshwater, 71–74
Allis shad, 147
Amoeba, 89
Angelica sylvestris, 50
Annelids, 96–100
Ants, 137
Aphanomyces astaca, 33
Apium nudiflorum, fool's water-
  cress, 80
Arctic char, 21, **22**
Argulus, 116, **116**
Asellus, 64, 117, **117,** 194
Asphodel, bog, 70
Aster tripolium, sea aster, 64
Azolla filiculoides, 76

B

Barbel, 29, 151
Bass, large-mouthed, 156
  rock, 156
  sea, 156
Barnacles, 61
Beetle, great silver, **133**
  whirligig, 133
Beetles, 130, 133
Bilberry, 70
Bistort, amphibious, 81
Bittern, 13
Blackbird, 8
Blackflies, 37
Bleak, 153
Bogbean, 82
Bog myrtle, 70
Bracken, 70
Bream, common, 3, 54, **54,** 151
  white, 153
Breydon Water, 10
Bridgewater Canal, 6
Bristle worms, 96

British Trust for Ornithology
  (BTO), 159, 165
Bugs, water, 127
Bullhead, 2, **27,** 27–28, **29,** 81,
  157, **157,** 158
Bulrush, 5
Bunting, reed, 5, 176–177, **176**
Buoyancy, 16
Burbot, 155
Bure, River, 10
Butterfly, swallowtail, **48,** 50
Butterwort, 67, 69

C

Caddisfly, 64, 134–135, 137
Canadian pondweed, 8, 77
Caraphractus cinctus, 137
Carp, common, 151
  crucian, 151
Carrot, wild, 50
Cataclysta lemnata, 136
Cerophium, 64
Chaeborus crystallinus, 136
China mark moth, 135, **136**
Chlamydomonas, 72
Chub, 3, 54, **54, 150,** 151
Cinclus cinclus, 37
Cladophora, 74
Clogging, 84, **84**
Cockles, 61
Cockshoot Broad, 14
Coelenterata, 91
Coenagrion armatum, 120
Coenagrion scitulum, 120
Coot, 51
Corixidae, 129
Cormorant, 178
Cotton grass, 69
Cowberry, 70
Coypu, 13, 191–192
Crab, shore, 60
Crake, spotted, 201
Cranefly, 137
Crayfish, **30,** 32–33, 118
Cricket, water, **127,** 127–128
Cross leaved heath, 70
Crustaceans, 111–118
Crystalwort, 75
Curlew, 160, **160**
Cyclops, 114, **115**
Cypria, 114

D

Dab, 55, 158
Dace, 154–155
Daddy-long-legs, *see* Cranefly
Damselflies, 121, 123–126, **131**
Daphnia, 111, **112, 113,** 113–114
Dee, River, 56
Demoiselle, 123
Dipper, 37, **168,** 169, 194
Diptera, 136–137
Diver, red throated, 159, 162
Dogwood, 8
Domesday Book, 10
Dotterel, 159
Dragonflies, 120–126, 137
Dragonfly, brown hawker, 51,
  51, 125
  club tailed, 121
  large red, 124
  southern hawker, **131**
Duck mussel, 103
Duckweeds, 76, **77**
Duddon, 56
Dunnock, 8
Dytiscus, 130–131, **130**

E

Eared snail, 108
Eden, River, **19**
Eel, common, 44, 46–47, 55, 155
Elder, 8
Ephemeroptera, *see* Mayflies
Eristalis, 137
Erobdella octoculata, 99
Estuary formation, 59
Eudorina, 72
Eye, of fish, 142, **143**
  of mammal, 143, **143**
Eyebright, 67

F

Fennel, 50
Ferns, 8
Fish farming, 199–201
Flatworms, 94–95
Flounder, 55, 158
Freshwater shrimp, 34, 118, **118**
Freshwater winkles, 109, **109**
Frog, common, 44
Frogbit, 76

G
Gas Works Acts, 19
Gerridae, *see* Pond skaters
Gills, 141–142
Gipsywort, 85
Glossiphonia complanata, 97
Glossiphonia heteroclita, 97
Gobies, 157
Goldeneye, 194
Goldfish, 152
Goosander, 164–165, **164**
Gordius, 95
Grand Trunk, **7**
Grayling, 3, **19,** 26–27, **26**
Grebe, great crested, 176
  little, 10, 42, 51
Greenpeace, 195
Grouse, red, 159, 163
Gudgeon, 152, **153**

H
Hare, brown, 159
Harrier, hen, 159, 162, **163**
  marsh, 13
Harts tongue fern, 76
Harvest mouse, 39–40, **40**
Hawthorn, 8
Heath bedstraw, 70
Hemiptera, *see* Bugs, water
Hemlock, water dropwort, 81
Heron, **vi,** 41, **168,** 169, 170–171, **171**
Herring, 55
Heysham atomic power station, 56
Hickling, 11
Himalayan balsam, 80
Hippuris vulgaris, 82
Hodder, River, **47,** 199, **199**
Holobdella stagnalis, 98
Horse leech, 99
Houting, 148
Humber, 8
Hydra, green, **92**
Hydroids, 91–92
Hydrometridae, *see* Water measurers

I
Insecticides, 5
Iris, yellow, 80, **80**
Ischnura elegans, 125
Itchen, River, 3

J
Jenkins' spire shell, 110

K
Keir, River, 56
Kent, River, 56, **64**
Kingfisher, 41, 51, **167,** 169, 171–172, **172**

L
Lacewings, **129,** 129–130
Lake limpet, 108
Lamprey, brook, 146
  river, 146
  sea, 147
Lapwing, 10, 166, **167,** 169
Lateral line, 140–141
Leech, medicinal, 50
Leeches, 97–99
Leven, River, 56
Liverworts, 75
Lizard, sand, 56
Loach, spined, 155
  stone, 28, **29,** 155
Louse, water, 64
Lousewort, *see* Rattle, red
Lune, River, 56

M
Maidenhair, spleenwort, 76
Mallard, 10, 51, 175–176, 194
Marestail, 82
Marsh marigold, **66**
Marsh snail, 107
Martin, sand, 57, 177–178
Mayflies, 35, **36,** 119–120
Meadowsweet, 85
Mersey, River, 6–8
Mestocharis bimacularis, 137
Milk parsley, 50
Miller's thumb, *see* Bullhead
Mink, 190–191
Minnow, 3, **30,** 31, 151
Mite, water, **138,** 138
Molluscs, 101–109
Monkey flower, 79–80
Moorhen, 51
Morecambe Bay, 56, 61
Moss animalcules, 93–94
Mosses, 75
Mullet, thick lipped, 158

N
Nematodes, 95–96
Nerite, 109
Neuroptera, *see* Lacewings
Newt, common, 44
  great crested, 43
  palmated, 43

Norfolk Broads, 10, **11, 14,** 14, 41
Norfolk Naturalists' Trust, 11
Notonectidae, 128

O
Oligochaeta, *see* Bristle worms
Orb mussel, 105
Orfe, 154–155
Osier, common, 83
Osprey, 10, 194
Ossifragum, see Asphodel, bog
Otter, 39, 182–188, **183, 184, 185, 187, 188**
Owl, short-eared, 162
Oystercatcher, 57, 173–174, **174**

P
Painter's mussel, 103
Pandorina, 72
Pea mussel, 104
Pearl mussel, 103
Perch, 143, **150, 156,** 156–157, 158
Peregrine falcon, 196
Periwinkles, 61
Phantom midge, 136–137
Phryganea grandis, 135
Pike, 148, **148**
Pisciola geometra, 97
Plaice, 55, 158
Platycnemis pennipes, 123
Plecoptera, *see* Stoneflies
Pleurococcus, 90
Plover, ringed, 57, 174
Pochard, 10
Polypody fern, 76
Polyzoa, 93–94
Pond skaters, 128, **131**
Pond snails, 107–108, **107**
Pond sponge, 90
Prawn, estuarine, 60
Pumpkinseed, 156

R
Rabbit, 159
Ragged robin, 88
Rail, water, 42
Ramshorn snail, 105, **106**
Ranworth, 14
Rat, brown, **189,** 189–190
Rat-tailed maggot, 137
Rattle, red, **66,** 68
  yellow, 68
Redshank, 10, 166–167, **167**
Reed cutting, **12**
Ring ouzel, 159

River limpet, 108
River management, 201–203
River sponge, 90
Roach, 3, 153–154
Robin, 8
Rochdale Canal, 8
Rotifers, 100, **100**
Royal Society for the Protection
    of Birds (R.S.P.B.), 13
Rudd, 3, **150,** 153–154
Rue, wall, 76
Ruffe, 156

S
Sage, wood, 70
Salmon, 24, 25, 55
Salmon ladder, **25**
Sandpiper, common, 172–173,
    173
  green, 201
Seal, common, 55
Severn, River, 56
Sewage farms, 201
Shad, 147
Shoveler, 10
Shrew, water, **181,** 181–182
Shrimp, common, 60
Simuliidae, *see* Blackflies
Skullcap, 88
Smelt, 148
Snipe, 10, 165–166
Sole, 55
Somerset levels, 41
Sparrowhawk, 196
Spartina grass, 57–59, **58**
Spearwort, lesser, 83
Speedwell, common, 70
Spirogyra, 73
Sponges, freshwater, 90–91
Spongilla fly, 91
Stalactites and stalagmites, 18
Stickleback, three-spined, 3, 45–
    46, **48,** 155
  ten-spined, 155
Stonefly, 34–35, 126–127
Stoneworts, 74–75, **74**
Stour, River, **186**
Strumpshaw Broad, 13
Sturgeon, 55, 147

Sundew, **66, 68,** 69
Surface film, 16
Swan, Bewick's, 175
  mute, 51, 174
  whooper, 175
Swan mussel, 51, 174
Swim bladder, 139

T
Teal, 10, 194
Temperature, 15
Tench, 152
Tern, black, 10
  little, 57
Thames estuary, 61
Thatching, 10
Theromyzon tessulatum, 98
Thrift, 64
Thrush, song, 8
Tit, bearded, 13
Toad, common, 44
  natterjack, 44, 56, **56**
Tormentil, 70
Trout, brown, 2, 22–23, **23, 149**
  rainbow, 22, **23,** 147, 200
Tubifex, 64
Tufted duck, 10
Twaite shad, 147

U
Ulothrix, 74

V
Valve shells, 109
Veliidae, *see* Cricket, water
Vendace, 147
Vole, bank, 41
  water, 41, 179–181, **180**
Voles, 159
Volvox, 72

W
Wagtail, grey, 37, **38,** 169
  pied, 8, **38**
  yellow, 38, **38**
Wandering snail, 108
Warbler, Cetti's, 42
  marsh, 42

reed, 42
Savi's, 43
sedge, 42
Wash, 56, 61
Wasps, 137
Water authorities, 20
Water boatmen, 128
  lesser, 129
Water clarity, 16
Water cress, 80
Water cricket, *see* Cricket, water
Water crowfoot, 3, 79
Water dropwort, 81
Water lilies, 77
Water measurers, 128
Water soldier, **12,** 77
Water spider, 138
Waterways Bird Survey, *see*
  British Trust for Orni-
  thology
Waveney, River, 10
Wels, 155
Wheel animalcules, 100, **100**
Whimbrel, 160, **160, 161**
Whirligigs, **132,** 133
Whirlpool trumpet shell, 106
Whitefish, 147
Whitethroat, 43, 178
Wigeon, 10
Willow, crack, 83
  moss, 75
  pussy, 83
  weeping, 83
  white, 83
Willowherb, great hairy, 88
  narrow leaved, 88
  small flowered, 88
  square stalked, 88
Woundwort, marsh, 88
Wren, 8

Y
Yare, River, 10
Yellow flag, 80

Z
Zander, 157
Zebra mussel, 104